JUST JACK

KATE SCOTT

Illustrated by Alexandra Gunn

Piccadilly
PRESS

First published in Great Britain in 2018 by
PICCADILLY PRESS
80–81 Wimpole St, London W1G 9RE
www.piccadillypress.co.uk

Text copyright © Kate Scott, 2018
Illustrations copyright © Alexandra Gunn, 2018

A CIP catalogue record for this book is available from the British Library.

ISBN: 978-1-84812-624-4
also available as an ebook

1 3 5 7 9 10 8 6 4 2

MIX
Paper from
responsible sources
FSC® C018072

This book is typeset by Perfect Bound Ltd
Printed and bound by Clays Ltd, St Ives Plc

Piccadilly Press is an imprint of Bonnier Zaffre Ltd,
a Bonnier Publishing company
www.bonnierpublishing.com

For my son, Noah, who gave me all
the best bits in this book.

Essentials

I'm Jack.

This is how I look now.

Here's how I looked six months ago.

And six months before that.

And six months before that.

In the last two years, we've moved house five times. I know a *lot* about packing.

I also know that some things are worth taking with you when you leave, and some aren't. Like your hobbies and interests. Because if there's one thing I've learned more than anything else, it's this:

If being yourself doesn't work out, try becoming someone else.

Mum in Move Mode

It was Moving Day and Mum was trying to find the mugs and teaspoons. If I didn't help her she'd still be looking this time next Wednesday.

'I don't understand,' she told me. 'I opened the box labelled "tea stuff".' She gestured at the open box at her feet.

I peered inside at the pile of saucepans, two tins of baked beans, a tin opener and a bath sponge.

'That was for dinner,' I told her. 'For later, remember? You didn't want us to have to cook properly straight after the move.' (The bath sponge was just the usual Mum wild card.)

Mum slapped her forehead. 'Oh yes! Of course . . . *tea* not tea . . .' She looked round her at the sea of boxes as if the right one might suddenly shout, 'Here I am!'

I walked over to a clear plastic box by the door and

lifted it up onto the kitchen table. 'See? I told you this was easier.' I pointed at the transparent walls of the box, which showed some bubble wrap around the edge of what was clearly a mug.

'Jack, you're a lifesaver.' Mum started to prise off the lid.

I went to fill the kettle, which I'd unpacked earlier. 'Next time –' I started, but Mum interrupted.

'I told you, sweetheart, there isn't going to be a next time. Things are different now.'

I didn't reply. Mum's sure that everything has changed and that we're going to stay settled here forever. But I know she's wrong. We've moved so often in such a short space of time that I can't imagine us doing anything else. Moving is what Mum and I do.

Sherlock Code

About half an hour later Mum sent me to the shop at the bottom of our road to buy some biscuits.

There was a girl and a boy of about my age hanging around outside, next to a low brick wall. My new school was only two streets away so I figured they probably went to it. I slowed down so I could follow Sherlock code. Sherlock code is the survival strategy I came up with when I realised that we were going to be moving house as often as some people go to the dentist.

The first part of Sherlock code is: Watch, Look and Listen. (This is also useful for crossing roads.)

I took in as much as possible, shooting them sideways glances so they didn't think I was staring.

Neither of them was wearing football kit on a Saturday.

The girl had on a Captain America T-shirt.

The boy was in an Iron Man T-shirt and a baseball cap.

Both of them were wearing bright red Converse.

As I passed them and went into the shop, I heard a snatch of their conversation.

'SnarkyMark's new post was seriously hilarious,' Iron Man said. 'Even Mum cracked up!'

'Yeah, so hilarious,' replied Captain America, and they both started laughing. Whatever SnarkyMark was, it must be pretty funny to make them fall about like that.

Sherlock code notes:

The boy and the girl were obviously brother and sister, maybe twins given they looked the same age.

The new school probably wasn't a sporty one like Schools Three and Five.

This was a relief. I like sport but School Three's idea of fun had been track running – *every single weekend.* One of the teachers there was an ex-Olympic runner, and he'd decided that if he couldn't be a professional athlete any more, he could at least try to produce a few. I was pretty sure he was going to succeed, because by the time I got there all anyone talked about was best times – and they meant racing, not hanging out with your friends. School Five was similar, but they were only focused on football. Everyone *there* thought you were weird if you didn't spend every spare moment down at the local club. The only fights that ever broke out were if someone said they supported a team that wasn't Man U.

The T-shirts were a good sign too. Schools Two and Four had been massively into Marvel, so I was ahead. (I can tell anyone everything they want to know about Iron Man – and probably a few things they don't.)

That only left one unknown – SnarkyMark – and I'd deal with that as soon as I got home. I just hoped SnarkyMark was as funny as Captain America and Iron Man T-shirt seemed to think it was.

It was a good start. When I left the shop I had more than a packet of biscuits; I had my first tips on how I was going to survive at School Six.

SnarkyMark

It turned out that SnarkyMark was a YouTuber. He basically talked about all the things he couldn't stand. After watching his posts, I couldn't help wondering if there was anything he actually liked. Brussels sprouts and Marmite came top of the list, but SnarkyMark also hated queues, blue cheese, itchy woolly jumpers, bus shelters that don't keep you from getting wet when it rains, chewing gum stuck in random places, maths tests, school roast potatoes, gravy that's too thick, gravy that's too thin, the smell of changing rooms, and paper clips. I agreed with him about most of it, apart from the paper clips – I didn't get that one. But SnarkyMark managed to go on about them for a full five minutes (apparently paper clips are too bendy).

SnarkyMark's posts involved cartoon flames, angry emojis and a sound effect like a cat when you tread on its tail by mistake. In half an hour I'd got the gist and was pretty sure I could come across as someone who'd been watching him all along.

In a way I understood SnarkyMark wanting to talk about all the things he hates. I've had to pretend to like a lot of things since we started moving. Starting a new school is like walking into a jungle with an 'Eat Me' sign around your neck. And that's the reason I take on a new personality every time we move. It isn't because I believe in lying; it's because I believe in surviving.

Funny Voices

When I was really little, maybe three or four, Dad went away for a few weeks to look after my grandmother after she had an operation. Up to then it had mostly been Dad who took me to nursery and looked after me at home. I loved it. With Dad, ordinary routines turned into proper events. At bath time, he'd whip up bubbles into huge peaks and then make my bath toys chase me through the bubble-clouds, chanting, 'Coming to get you!' And he didn't mind me making him endless cups of bubble-bath tea in my red plastic tea set. He'd pretend to drink it and smack his lips as if it was the most delicious thing he'd ever (not) tasted.

Another thing he was good at was voices. When he read stories to me he would do low growly voices and high squeaky ones and different accents for all the characters. Mum said his Dorset accent sounded Welsh and the rest of his accents sounded Australian, but I didn't care. Words were funnier and brighter when he was the one saying them.

Dad would dress up for story time too. When we were out he'd insist we went into every charity shop to look for the oddest and most colourful clothes we could find. We ended up with a ton of stuff in our dressing-up box. There was a huge straw hat with a broad blue band, and a silky red cape. There was a long blue-and-white stripy scarf and even a fake fur coat that he put on for any story involving snow.

When he was reading, he walked up and down the room, gesturing with the hand that wasn't holding the book. Mum used to tell him off, saying that his storytelling didn't help me get to sleep; it woke me up. But she always smiled when she said it, and sometimes she'd creep in to listen too.

So when he went away that first time, I really missed him. I missed the bath toys chasing me through bubble-clouds and his deep growly voice reading *The Gruffalo* and the blue-and-white stripy scarf. I even missed the smell of him.

The day he was due back, Mum drove us to the airport to meet him as a surprise. I remember how she hoisted me up on her hip so that I could look for him and how, when I saw him appear, his face all stubbly and his hair flat on one side from where he'd slept against the plane window, I'd started whispering, 'Dad, my dad!' I'd stretched out my arms as if they were long enough to reach him even though he was still at the other end of the arrivals hall. And when he caught sight of us and broke into a wide grin, I felt so light I thought I might take off and fly right out of Mum's arms.

The Trouble Ninja

Mum's the only person I know who's capable of losing a second thing while she's still looking for the first thing. For instance, she'll go into the bathroom to brush her teeth and notice that we're nearly out of toilet paper. So she'll head out to the kitchen to write down 'toilet paper' on our shopping list, but not be able to find a pen. Then she'll go to her office (usually a desk in the corner of the living room) and see an email alert. Ten minutes later I'll find her with her toothbrush tucked behind her ear, laughing at a cat video on YouTube.

But even though she's a bit scatterbrained day to day, Mum's always been good at dealing with trouble. If something big happens, she instantly turns into a Trouble Ninja. When she's in Trouble Ninja mode, you could put my mum in front of someone who'd accidentally chopped off their finger and she wouldn't even blink; she'd just pick it up and figure out a way to sew it back on.

It's probably because up until this last move Mum was a telly producer, which is one of those jobs where you're always being presented with a crisis. So she learned how to deal with them without getting stressed. It's quite funny to watch the transformation. When Mum is being her everyday self, she goes around leaving banana skins on top of the washing machine, or pinning half her hair up and then losing track and leaving the other half down. But when there's trouble, she gets all steely-eyed and glinty. Even her voice changes and becomes slow and calm, like someone trying to hypnotise you, or talk you out of doing something extreme. It's almost as if she doesn't know you – she's just a professional doing her job.

That's what she was like the night Dad left. She helped him pack his bags and load the car with her steely Trouble Ninja expression on her face the whole time.

You wouldn't have guessed that he'd ever meant anything to us at all.

Inside and Out

There's this expression about knowing someone inside and out. But with me that's not possible. Because there's the me you see *outside* my house and then there's the me I am with my mum *inside* the house. Whenever we move, I always feel a bit jittery until I figure out what kind of person I need to become, because until then it's like being in a play when you haven't seen the script.

But at home I knew exactly who to be. And right now Mum looked exhausted.

'Do you want me to make dinner?'

Mum looked up from the box she was unpacking. It was definitely one of the ones she'd been in charge of, because what she'd pulled out so far was a duvet, a bottle of kitchen-surface cleaner, her jewellery box and five plastic plant pots.

'Oh, *would* you? I was wondering where I was going to get the energy to feed us.'

'No problem.'

I went off to work out the new grill. Mum isn't bad at cooking, but she's never really enjoyed it, so as soon as I was old enough to hold a knife without her freaking out, I took over.

After digging around I found the tea towels and put one over my arm. Then I went back to where Mum had collapsed on the sofa. 'Just to check the menu – would madam like green beans poached in peanut butter? Or perhaps tomato paste with chocolate marshmallows? Or maybe some eggs with pineapple, seaweed and chilli pepper?'

Mum tapped her mouth with her finger, considering. 'I think I'd like some sweetcorn tossed with chocolate raisins, pickles, sardines and maybe a dash of maple syrup, please.'

Mum and I have an ongoing competition to try and come up with the most disgusting-sounding dish. She usually wins, probably because of the TV show she produced a few years ago – *Can't Cook, Cooks Anyway* – which was about people who thought that Brussels sprout ice cream was a good idea. I bowed low to the ground. 'Excellent choice.'

I made beans on toast and brought it over to the sofa so we could eat on our laps in front of the telly. (I'd put the plates and cutlery in one of the clear boxes – Mum might be better at inventing fake nasty meals, but when it came to packing I won every time.) Mum blew me a kiss. 'You, Jack, are completely wonderful.'

That was the thing though. Inside me was easy to be – it was Outside me that was tricky.

Nine Minutes to Live

I'd been right about the Marvel twins. They did go to my school and they were even in my class. Their names were Libby and Isaac and they gave me a nod when I arrived. I went to the back where Mr Tull, my new Year Six teacher, had told me to sit.

Moving around so much, I'd got used to lots of different types of teachers. Mr Tull was what I called a high-energy teacher (they don't stay still much and they wave their hands around a lot when they explain things). Other teacher types I've come across include low-energy teachers (big on 'quiet time'), shouty teachers (never want to hear your side), smiley-but-deadly teachers (nice to grown-ups but super-strict with kids) and fun teachers (always coming up with random projects like making historical figures out of jelly).

'Great to have you with us, Jack,' Mr Tull told me, clapping his hands together. 'I'm sure you'll find us a friendly bunch. Do you want to tell us a bit about yourself to start with?'

I usually hate getting this question too early, but this time, thanks to Libby and Isaac, I was ahead.

'Um, yeah, well, I like watching SnarkyMark,' I said, shrugging my shoulders to look casual.

Mr Tull laughed. 'Do you now? Well, Jack, you're going to fit right in. Nearly everyone in this class *loves* a bit of SnarkyMark.'

I smiled, like this was a surprise. Out of the corner of my eye I saw Libby and Isaac exchanging a look of approval. So I probably had two in my corner, maybe more if what Mr Tull had said was true.

Following Sherlock code means getting two or three 'safe friends' as a buffer so you can disappear into the background. Isaac and Libby might be perfect. It was starting to look like Move Six could go smoothly.

Then another boy showed up.

'Tyler!' Mr Tull called. 'Nice of you to turn up – outrageously late as usual.'

'I've got the best reason though, sir,' Tyler said. He had black curly hair that went in all directions and a big toothy grin. His school jumper was covered in little badges. They all had quotes on them but I couldn't see what they said.

'Really.' Mr Tull looked like someone who had been through a form of this conversation a lot. He had the same kind of expression on his face that I probably have when Mum tells me she's lost something – again.

'I've found the answer to nagging parents *and* twisted toothpaste tubes,' Tyler told him. 'I took a basic toothpaste lever that squishes toothpaste from the bottom and adapted it to play music for two minutes so you know when you've brushed for long enough. It's one of my best two-for-one ideas.'

Tyler was obviously not someone who had any problems with confidence.

'Right,' Mr Tull said. He didn't seem surprised to hear that someone in his class was inventing gadgets before breakfast. 'And that had to happen before school because . . . ?'

Tyler held out his hands. 'That's when I had the idea!'

Mr Tull shook his head. 'Please try and have – or at least act on – your ideas in your own time, Tyler.'

'I'll try, sir, but you never know when genius is going to strike.'

'I'm more interested in your knowing when the hour

to get to school is going to strike,' Mr Tull said – but I noticed he was smiling.

Mr Tull took the rest of the register while Tyler sat down, mouthing a silent 'hi' to me. I nodded, thinking that although I'd love to know more about the toothpaste squeezer, Tyler definitely didn't qualify as a safe friend.

Tyler didn't qualify as shy either.

As soon as the bell rang for break, he appeared at my side, bouncing on his heels. 'Hey.'

'Hi.' I glanced down and noticed his shoes. They were bright green trainers with laces that had lots of weird feathery things on them.

He saw me looking. 'Fishing Shoes,' he said. 'So you can go fly fishing at a moment's notice. I invented them for my dad. These are just the prototype.'

I didn't even know what fly fishing was (it couldn't be fishing for *flies*, could it?) and I wasn't absolutely sure what a prototype was either. I didn't ask though. Not saying too much is part of Sherlock code.

Tyler pushed his hair out of his face and I saw that he had a row of colourful cord bracelets around his wrist. Now he was standing closer, I could see that one of his badges said 'Busy Being Amazing'. I'd met a lot of people in all my schools, but I hadn't met anyone quite like Tyler before.

'Right,' Tyler said. 'Nine minutes to live, what do you do?' He looked at me expectantly.

'Um . . . don't know really.' I shifted my backpack onto the table, unzipped it and started rummaging around in it as if I was looking for something. Surely Tyler would get the hint and move on to someone else.

But he didn't. 'Tell you what, I'll tell you what *I'd* do, because it's perfect, and then you have your turn,' Tyler said. He perched himself on the edge of the table, swinging his feet back and forth.

I looked round, hoping Mr Tull would see and tell Tyler to get down, but he was busy helping a girl called Zoe reach up for a bag of footballs to take outside.

'I'd call everyone I cared about and tell them the best memory I had of them,' Tyler said. 'Then I'd get myself straight down to the supermarket, buy a big bag of doughnuts and stuff my face.'

It sounded like a good plan. Though my only call would be to my mum and I'd probably go for dark chocolate, not doughnuts.

'I know what I'd do,' Zoe said, as she passed by with the footballs. 'I'd ring for an ambulance. That's what you do if you're dying, Tyler. You don't waste time buying doughnuts.'

'There isn't anyone to save you,' Tyler told her. 'You

are dying in nine minutes no matter what you do, so calling for an ambulance is wasting some of your last precious moments.'

'I don't give up hope. Ever. My mum says it's my best quality,' Zoe said, swinging the bag over her shoulder and only narrowly avoiding hitting Tyler in the face with it.

'No, look –' Tyler jumped down from the desk and followed her as she moved away – 'it's a *game* question, and the rules are that you have to accept the question as it is.'

'I don't have to accept anything, Tyler,' Zoe said.

Tyler turned around to me and pulled at his hair, opening his mouth in a silent 'ARGHHHH!' expression. I laughed. I couldn't help it. I was going to have to watch out – keeping my distance with Tyler was going to be hard.

Hilarious

In the end I didn't have to worry about Tyler at break because Libby and Isaac had decided that I was going to be their new mate. This sometimes happens at schools – a group decides to adopt me. I knew it was nice of them, but I couldn't help feeling a bit disappointed when I saw Tyler playing football with Zoe across the other side of the playground.

Not that I didn't like the twins – they seemed nice enough and they definitely qualified as 'safe'. But there was a slight problem. They only wanted to talk about one thing: SnarkyMark. They didn't just like SnarkyMark; they loved SnarkyMark. The only thing they disagreed on was which post was the funniest. Isaac would say something like, 'The best one was the one about sandwiches from petrol stations.' Then Libby would say, 'Yeah, that was hilarious. But the one about salad dressing was even better.' This was OK for about the first five minutes, but it didn't stop. The only other phrase they had was one of SnarkyMark's – 'Soooo bad it's evil.' When I asked them if they watched any other YouTubers, they looked at me like I'd lost control of my senses.

'No, because no one's as good as SnarkyMark, are they?' Libby said.

'Yeah, why would you want to watch someone else when you could be watching SnarkyMark?' Isaac said, nodding.

Because you'd had enough of SnarkyMark to last a lifetime? I thought. But I didn't say anything. I'd watched a few more SnarkyMark posts the night before and decided he wasn't quite as funny as he thought he was, but I was pretty sure Libby and Isaac wouldn't agree.

'I mean, we used to play Dragon Quest, but then it got boring,' said Libby.

'Yeah, and SnarkyMark is funnier. Like the one when he talks about playing Dragon Quest?'

Libby snorted. 'Hilarious!'

Libby and Isaac really liked the word 'hilarious'.

I wanted to tell them that I liked Dragon Quest and still played it. But that's not how Sherlock code works, so I took a breath, smiled and kept my mouth shut. Even after so many moves, I sometimes forgot how exhausting it was to become a brand-new person.

Keeping to the Rules

Even though I had my safety net of Isaac and Libby, I was determined not to pay too much attention to Tyler. It wasn't only that he didn't fall into the safe-friend category; he was so outgoing that I was worried that even sitting near him might make it impossible for me to fade into the background.

The problem is, it's hard not to pay attention to someone when they swing in ten minutes late and bounce up to the front of the class with a big grin on their face.

'What was it today, Tyler?' Mr Tull examined Tyler over the tops of his glasses in an effort to look serious. I didn't buy it for a minute – it was obvious that he wanted to know what Tyler had invented just as much as Tyler wanted to tell him.

'Nail Caps!' Tyler reached into his bag and pulled out

a handful of what looked like tiny colourful plastic bags.

'Excuse me?' Mr Tull got up to take a closer look.

'They're to help people who want to stop biting their nails,' Tyler said. He plucked out a few and dropped them in front of Zoe.

Zoe looked insulted for a second and then she picked one up. 'It's cute!'

'I know, right?' Tyler nodded. 'Fits snugly enough that you can go about doing your business, but every time you go to bite your nail . . . ?' He mimed trying to gnaw on a finger. 'Your teeth hit plastic!'

'Very clever indeed,' Mr Tull said, going back to his desk. 'If only you could show the same dedication to timekeeping and spelling.'

'Thanks, sir,' Tyler said, smiling at the compliment and ignoring the rest. 'I figured I can do them in lots of different themes and colours. And one that's designed specially for thumbs to help people who suck their thumb.'

'Your dedication to helping people is noted. Now, if I could take the register?' Mr Tull raised the register up in the air as if asking for permission.

'Oh sure, go ahead!' Tyler waved his hand, smiling.

You'd think Tyler acting as if he was in charge would land him in trouble, but he had a way of making everything sound like a joke so it was hard to get annoyed. At least, I guess it was that, because Mr Tull just shook his head, laughed and started taking the register.

Skater-Flyer Shoes

Later that morning, while we were working on the maths worksheet Mr Tull had handed out, I found myself trying to get a closer look at Tyler's shoes. They were silver and had what looked like levers on the heels.

He caught my glance and stuck out one of his feet proudly. 'They're my Skater-Flyer Shoes,' he said. 'I made them myself.'

'You *made* them?' The toothpaste squeezer and the Nail Caps I believed. I mean, I would never have thought of them or been able to make them myself, but it didn't seem completely incredible that someone my age could have come up with them. But the Skater-Flyer Shoes were on a whole different level. Especially if it turned out they actually worked. I stared as Tyler reached down to flick the lever on his left shoe. A row of wheels popped out underneath and two jet-like wings came out to the sides.

'Yeah,' Tyler said. 'You see, the roller shoes you get in the shops are a bit basic. I wanted to make something that gives more control – you can steer these, and they have four different speeds. I think they'd be good for people who have difficulty getting around.'

'That's really cool!' Even though I was trying not to be too friendly with Tyler, I couldn't help myself – the shoes *were* cool.

Tyler's face lit up. 'Yeah?'

'Definitely.' I bent down to look at the wings – it was like having a mini-747 attached to your shoes. 'It's great how all your inventions are to solve problems.'

'Yeah, they are.' Tyler looked at me thoughtfully. 'Not everyone sees that. I mean, they get the shoes, but not why I'd want to make something that helps someone to stop biting their nails, or pick their nose or something.'

'You made something to stop people picking their nose?'

'Well, no, but I'm working on it.'

I laughed.

'Everyone thinks I should concentrate on stuff like this –' Tyler pointed to his shoes – 'but I like making stuff that solves all kinds of problems.'

'Yeah, that makes sense.' I decided that s... already said something, I may as well go ahead an... honest. It was pretty obvious that Tyler probably w... a genius, at least when it came to creating things. The only thing I'd ever tried to make was a pair of bookends in School Three, and they'd been so disastrously bad that they'd knocked over any books we tried to put between them. (They went missing in Move Five and I had my suspicions that for once Mum had lost something on purpose.)

Tyler looked pleased. 'Thanks.' He pulled out a small yellow piece of plastic from his pocket. 'See this? It's a remote-controlled battery power pack so that I can use extra power if I want to.' He showed it to me – it had one switch on it, which seemed to have been made by melting a large button. As I was examining it, Mr Tull swooped in and scooped it up.

'I'll be taking that, Tyler,' he said. 'I think we had an agreement, didn't we? No remotes at school. And especially no remotes for Skater-Flyer Shoes. Remember what happened last time?'

Mr Tull turned to me. 'Tyler here thought it would be a great idea to help the lunch supervisors by taking round a platter of vegetables to serve up to everyone at the table. Unfortunately Tyler's Skater-Flyer Shoes, with the aid of this booster pack, made him go very fast indeed. It had unfortunate consequences.'

'It was a bit messy,' Tyler admitted.

Mr Tull raised an eyebrow. 'I don't think "a bit" covers it, Tyler. We were peeling flattened peas from the walls for *weeks*, and Ms Melville narrowly missed getting a carrot up her nose.'

'Sorry, sir,' Tyler said. It was the second time I'd heard him apologise without looking particularly sorry. I was pretty sure he was trying not to laugh.

'You can claim this back at the end of the day,' Mr Tull told Tyler, holding up the remote control. 'And please wear normal shoes tomorrow.'

'I don't have any normal shoes, sir. I've enhanced them all,' Tyler said with a grin.

It wasn't a rude grin, just a slightly cheeky one. To be honest, I could see why Mr Tull found it hard to get angry with Tyler.

'Well then,' Mr Tull said, 'make sure you don't use those enhancements unless it's out of school hours, all right? We all know you're an inventor or a creator or whatever, but some of your inventions present serious health-and-safety risks. Which tends to create serious issues for me.'

'Sure thing.'

'Now get back to that worksheet, both of you,' Mr Tull said. 'You can tell Jack what a genius you are over lunch, OK?'

'No probs, sir.' Tyler picked up his pen and went back to the maths. But when Mr Tull had returned to his desk he whispered, 'I'll show you how the power pack works later – I've got a spare remote.'

I nodded but I didn't say anything. I was trying to figure out how to salvage my survival strategy. Not only did I usually try to avoid getting to know any one person too well, I've also always made it a rule not to get into trouble. Getting into trouble attracts attention, and attention isn't good when all you want to do is lie low and get on with everyone.

The only thing was, I *really* wanted to see those Skater-Flyer Shoes in action.

SnarkyMark
Is Not a Greek God

At the start of lunch break Isaac and Libby were waiting for me by the door – it was clear they'd decided I was one of them now. Tyler glanced over and shrugged at me, as if to say, 'OK, if that's what you want.' Which it was – sort of.

It turned out the twins did have another interest apart from SnarkyMark. After lunch (when they'd gone over all the foods that SnarkyMark didn't like – which was such a large group that I did wonder how SnarkyMark managed not to starve), they started on what turned out to be their second hobby: making money.

'Do you get much pocket money, Jack?' Isaac asked me as we settled on one of the benches in the upper years' playground.

I shrugged. I didn't like giving any details about my

own home life until I had a better sense of everyone else's. 'The usual,' I said, hoping they wouldn't ask what the usual was.

'Yeah, not enough, right?' Libby said.

'Uh . . . right.' It seemed to be the safest answer.

'We've been working on some ideas to make some money,' Isaac said. 'You should come back to ours. We could tell you about our plan –'

'It's called Project Moneybags,' Libby broke in, and then laughed.

'Yeah, Moneybags,' Isaac said. 'Does what it says on the tin, yeah? Anyway, you could come back after school this week and we could tell you about it – see if you wanted to get involved, then watch some SnarkyMark classics.'

'OK,' I said. I wasn't all that interested in hearing about Project Moneybags. Or in watching more SnarkyMark. But I knew that if I wanted to become part of a group, even a small one, I needed to do what Isaac and Libby wanted.

That was one problem of fitting around other people's interests: no one was going to fit around yours.

The last period that afternoon was literacy. Mr Tull put us in pairs to write about Greek myths. Mr Tull put me with Tyler. Next to us, Zoe was with a girl called Dani. Even though I was nervous about getting too friendly with Tyler, it was a relief to get away from Isaac and Libby and their endless chat about SnarkyMark. I'd never heard *anyone* talk so much about *one* thing. I even heard them asking Mr Tull if they could write about SnarkyMark instead a myth.

'Unless SnarkyMark is a Greek god, no.'

'But, sir,' Isaac said, 'he's like a myth in the making. *Everyone* knows him.'

'I don't care if the entire universe is aware of SnarkyMark,' Mr Tull said. 'He's not Zeus so you won't be writing about him.'

I caught Tyler's eye. He smiled at me. 'Are you as big a fan of SnarkyMark as those two then?'

'Um . . .' I hesitated. I'd said in front of everyone that I liked SnarkyMark. I couldn't admit I was already sick of the sound of him.

Tyler gave me a look like he could read my mind. 'Sometimes you can like something for five minutes. But that doesn't mean you like it for five hours.' He nodded over to Isaac and Libby. 'I mean, there's only so much "hilarious" anyone can take, right?'

I couldn't help it. I laughed. 'Right,' I agreed.

Tyler grinned back and then turned to Zoe and Dani.

'OK then, who are you going to write about – how about Hermes? You could give him a pair of my enhanced shoes.'

'Don't go on about your enhanced shoes,' Zoe said. 'You're as bad as Libby and Isaac, you know. It's just a different subject.'

Tyler clutched his chest. 'I can't believe you said that! You're so cruel!'

Zoe sniffed. 'Oh, give over.'

'One day,' Tyler told her, 'when I'm the most famous inventor of the twenty-first century and people are clamouring to interview me, you'll be sorry you treated me like this. Come on, Jack, let's show these two how it's done.' He smacked his worksheet. 'Zoe, Jack and I hereby challenge you to a duel of the gods – our Greek myth against yours.'

Zoe sighed. 'Why do you have to turn everything into a competition?'

Tyler slapped the desk. 'Because life is a game! And I'm one hundred per cent about winning it!'

He turned to me, smiling. 'It's time for us to prove our brilliance. Ready?'

I shrugged and nodded. I wondered what it would be like to be confident the way Tyler was, to be so sure that everyone would accept you and like you – no matter how cheeky, or full of over-the-top confidence, you were.

But to be honest, I knew what it would be like. It would be great.

Two Invitations

After school, I tried to head out towards home as quickly as possible so that I could do some more Sherlock follow-up work. I'd made some notes about a couple of TV programmes Tyler, Zoe and Dani had been talking about when we were meant to be working on the Greek myth project and I planned to get up to speed on them that night.

'Hey, Jack!' Isaac came over as I was shrugging on my coat in the hallway. 'We thought we'd have that SnarkyMark marathon tomorrow. And we can tell you about our project too. You're still up for it, right?'

'Um, sure.'

'Great. Our mum works shifts, so if we're lucky we could get two or three hours straight.'

Two or three *hours* of SnarkyMark? I'd used up most of my interest in him already. But if Mum was determined to stay here, then I needed to make sure I fitted in. So instead of saying something like, 'Thanks, but actually tomorrow I'm having all of my teeth extracted without anaesthetic which will still be more fun than watching SnarkyMark and talking about how to get mega-rich,' I said, 'Cool, thanks.'

Isaac and Libby went off and I turned to pick up my bag. I almost yelled in shock because Tyler was standing right there next to me. He had a funny expression on his face and I realised he must have overheard our conversation. 'Guess you aren't that tired of SnarkyMark after all,' he said.

'Oh, I . . . SnarkyMark's OK really,' I said. I felt my face flush. Something about the way Tyler was looking at me made me feel uncomfortable.

Tyler picked up his own bag. 'If you say so. But if you ask me, it's better to be honest than to worry about being rude,' he said. 'People figure out the truth eventually anyway.'

A nasty shiver went down the back of my neck. It felt like what Tyler meant was: *They'll figure out you're a fake sooner or later.* Which was pretty much my worst fear through every move Mum and I had made. It was exactly why I tried not to make close friends.

I couldn't think of the best way to respond so I didn't

say anything. That's standard Sherlock code anyway – say as little as possible until you're sure you'll say the right thing.

Tyler waited. Then he gave me a smile that somehow made me feel like he'd read my mind. 'Well, anyway, if you change your mind about wanting to *enjoy* a marathon of SnarkyMark, you can always come over to mine. I've got a ton of stuff I could show you, like this.' He took a remote out of his pocket and pressed it. Immediately his shoes rose up above the ground and the wings he'd shown me earlier popped out and then angled downwards. Tyler leaned forward and took off along the corridor, the wheels and wings making a whirring noise as he sped along the lino floor.

Mr Tull popped his head out of the classroom. 'Tyler! What did I say about –'

'Sorry, sir, got to go!' Tyler caught the edge of the door as it was closing behind someone else up ahead, swung himself round and waved back at both of us before disappearing.

'That boy . . .' Mr Tull shook his head, then saw me looking. He smiled. 'If you make friends with Tyler, Jack, I can guarantee your life will never be boring.'

All the way home I couldn't stop thinking about what Mr Tull had said. I'd never met anyone like Tyler before, and I definitely liked him – it was impossible not to – but boring was what I'd always aimed for. It felt safe. Boring might not be what most people wanted from life, but for me, boring worked.

Project Moneybags

Isaac's room was a shrine to two things – SnarkyMark and money. Every wall was covered in posters. There were stills from SnarkyMark videos, and posters of SnarkyMark's Top Hates (vegetable smoothies, someone farting when you're in a lift and your favourite show not being available on Netflix). There were also loads of pieces of paper with quotes about making money on them. One said '"Rule Number 1. Never lose money. Rule Number Two. Never forget Rule Number One." *Warren Buffet*.'

Isaac saw me reading the quote and pointed to Warren Buffet's name. 'That man is the business.'

Libby nodded. '*We'll* be the business soon.'

They high-fived and then did a screaming cat noise which made me jump. 'What was that?'

Isaac and Libby stared at me. 'SnarkyMark's

signature, yeah?' Isaac looked a bit horrified that I hadn't recognised it.

'Oh yeah. Course.'

Isaac and Libby sank down on two beanbags and gestured to me to take the third one.

Then I took in all the stuff around me. Apart from the bed and the beanbags, there was a desk, an office chair, a side table with a PlayStation on it, and a bookshelf that didn't have any books but had a pile of chargers, three tablets, six MP3 players, nine mobile phones, four different piggy banks (two in the form of mini-safes) and a stack of games. There were piles of clothes on the bed and in an open wardrobe, and about seven jackets hanging on the back of the door.

Libby laughed when she saw me staring. 'Isaac, Jack thinks all that's yours!'

Isaac laughed too. 'Nah, that's all part of Project Moneybags, see?'

I didn't.

Isaac leaned forward and lowered his voice. 'Right, so the thing is, we all want to make some serious money, yeah?'

'Serious,' said Libby, nodding again.

'What we've been doing is buying people's old phones and stuff,' Isaac said, 'and then selling them on eBay –

our mum's got an account – so we can make a bit of extra pocket money.'

'But it's not much.' Libby held up her thumb and forefinger to illustrate how tiny the amount was.

'Yeah,' Isaac said. 'Not much.'

'Right,' I said. They were both looking at me expectantly. I had no idea what they wanted me to say. But the good thing about staying quiet is that if you do it for long enough, someone will usually break the silence.

'See,' Isaac said, 'what we need is something good to sell. Not old stuff – new stuff.'

'Something people haven't seen before,' Libby said, nodding again. She reminded me of one of those toy dogs with its neck on wire so its head goes up and down all the time.

'Right,' I said again. They were still looking at me as if waiting for me to understand what they were getting at. The problem was, I didn't.

'You sit next to Tyler in class, yeah?' Isaac sat back up.

'Uh, yeah?' Now I had an idea, but I didn't know if it was right.

'He makes loads of cool stuff, yeah?' Isaac said. (Libby nodded.)

'Right . . .'

'We've been thinking that what he needs is some expert help,' Isaac said. 'See, to make money you need good stuff to sell.' Then he raised his hands to illustrate the punchline. 'But you also need a way to sell it. My brother says that's called marketing. He's doing it at college as part of his business studies. So we'd do that.'

It was getting clearer now.

'So, see, Ty's got the product and we've got the skills.'

'Because of eBay?' I didn't want to be rude, but I didn't think that selling things on your mum's eBay account really counted as 'skills'.

Isaac laughed and Libby shook her head. (It made a change from the nodding.)

'No, no,' Isaac said. 'We're going to make our own website. It's going to be seriously good. Our own company.'

'Serious,' Libby said, back to nodding.

'What's it going to be called?' I was buying time, figuring out what to say. I understood now that the twins wanted to sell Tyler's inventions. What I didn't understand was why they were talking to me about it and not him.

'You. Seriously. Need. This. Stuff.' Isaac jabbed the air as he said each word.

'So good,' Libby said.

To be honest, I thought the company name needed work. Seriously. But it wasn't the right time to say so.

'We could make a ton of money. A *ton*,' Isaac said. 'We'll make Project Moneybags *big*.'

'Really big.'

'So you've talked to Tyler?' I thought I'd better get to the point.

Isaac and Libby glanced at each other and then Isaac brought up his hand and waggled it. 'Well, sort of . . . but he's not sure he wants to.'

'So if he doesn't want to sell his stuff . . .'

'What we need,' Isaac said, 'is a way to convince him.'

'And since he likes you, he might listen if *you* say something,' Libby said.

'He likes everyone though – he has loads of friends.'

'Yeah, he's friendly to everyone, but he's always so busy inventing things he doesn't usually hang out with just one person,' Isaac said. 'But you two seem to get on really well.'

'Yeah. Way better than anyone else.' Libby smiled, nodding at me encouragingly.

I thought about it. It was true; I hadn't seen Tyler with anyone in particular. He chatted with whoever was around, but he didn't seem to have a best friend. Maybe he was a bit of a loner. Maybe that was the reason he stood out so much. Apart from being an inventor of amazing gadgets. It was nice thinking that Isaac and Libby thought Tyler liked me. That he could be my friend.

'So we thought – maybe you could get to know him and then explain how good we are at marketing stuff.' Isaac looked hopefully at me. 'Tell him we're the best, yeah? We've got loads of ideas.'

'Loads.' Libby held out her arms. 'The two of us are like an ideas machine.'

I remembered what Tyler had said about wanting to make things to help people. I couldn't be sure, but I wasn't convinced that Tyler would be impressed by Project Moneybags.

The twins were supposed to be my way of keeping in the background, and now they wanted me to spend more time with the one person I'd decided wouldn't be a safe friend. And the weirdest thing? It was exactly what I wanted to do.

Resistance Is Futile

The next morning Tyler yanked out his chair and sank down next to me. I was impressed – he wasn't late. But, as always, he had something to say. 'Did you ever name one of your toys something funny when you were little?'

I thought about the toy shark Dad had given me and how we'd come up with his name. Then I thought about all the times we'd named things and how seriously Dad had always taken it, even pulling out the copy of *Baby Names* that he and Mum had used to help them decide what to call me.

'When I was four, I named my first teddy Fishy Pie,' Tyler went on. 'And the next one Ketchup.'

I laughed.

'And my sister, Abby,' Tyler went on, 'called *her* teddy Farty Pants.'

'Please don't tell me what she called the next one,' Mr Tull said, appearing beside us.

Tyler laughed. 'You wouldn't guess – it was Limey Germ.'

'Interesting thought processes in your household,' Mr Tull said. 'Anyone else?'

'I had six dolls. I called them all Bob,' Zoe said.

'How did you tell them apart?' Dani asked.

Zoe shrugged. 'Easy – BobOne, BobTwo, BobThree . . .'

Everyone laughed, and I don't know what got into me but I found myself saying, 'I had a toy shark called Geoffrey B. Stapleton.' I didn't mention that I still had him, and that he was on a shelf in my room.

I got the laugh I'd been looking for, but inside I was already regretting it. Geoffrey B. Stapleton was something real from my past, and I'd always promised to keep things like that secret.

A boy called James started talking about his two toy rhinos, Bertie and Gertie, and Mr Tull laughed as he listened.

'If we're lucky, this will last right through Mr Tull's first lesson plan,' Tyler whispered, grinning at me. I grinned back.

Maybe there wasn't any harm in getting to know

Tyler a bit better. Then at some point I could tell him about Isaac and Libby's scheme to sell his inventions for Project Moneybags and it wouldn't matter if he said yes or no.

I'd be like Tyler was – friendly with everyone but no one's best friend. Keeping my distance just enough to keep to my code.

Geoffrey
B. Stapleton

Dad bought me the shark for my fifth birthday. Later he told me that he'd wanted to get something different from all the toy teddies, bunnies and puppies. When he gave it to me, he told me in a very serious voice that the naming ceremony would be at bedtime. Mum had laughed, but Dad had kept his solemn expression and whispered to me, 'You know he's magic, right?'

That night, Dad had put the shark in the middle of the floor and got me to sit cross-legged in front of it. Then he sat facing me, with the shark in the middle. Dad leaned forward, resting his chin on his hands, and gazed at it. 'Now we wait.'

'What for?' I'd asked.

Dad looked at me. 'For him to tell us his name, of course!'

We sat in silence for a while, staring at the shark. I got the giggles, but Dad didn't even crack a smile. After a minute or two, he tipped his head towards the shark. 'Did you hear that?'

I stopped laughing and crouched down right beside it. I shook my head.

Dad got even closer. 'What's that? Oh!'

He sat up straight. 'He says his first name is Geoffrey.'

I remember wondering whether it was possible that my dad really could hear toys talk. I stared as he leaned in close again. 'Oh, how nice of you.'

He smiled at me. 'He wants you to give him his middle name and his surname, Jack. That's a real honour, you know.'

We pulled out some of my books to search for possibilities and eventually I decided on 'Bertram' for his middle name, after a story that Dad used to read me – *Bertram and his Fabulous Animals*. I said he would call himself 'Geoffrey B.' for short. But I couldn't decide on a last name. Mum came in and made suggestions and we ended up calling out names until it was way past my bedtime. I can't even remember how we came up with 'Stapleton' – I can only remember how hard the three of us were laughing by the time Geoffrey B. finally had his name.

Luke Skywalker's Christmas Present

On Friday, Mr Tull told us we'd be having a science afternoon, learning about electricity and circuits. He brought out a pile of wires and miniature bulbs and explained that we would be soldering the wires together – 'Under my close supervision,' he said, looking hard at us all.

Then he pointed at Tyler. 'Now, Tyler, I know that you'll be wanting to turn this project into one of your inventions, but you need to stick to the instructions. Understood?' He turned to me. 'Jack, you're clearly the most sensible one of the two of you so I'm relying on you to keep him in line, OK?'

I nodded, though from what I'd seen so far, there was nothing that could stop Tyler from, well, being Tyler. I glanced over at him, but Tyler just raised his eyebrows innocently. 'It sounds like a great project, sir,' he said. 'Very inspiring.'

Mr Tull narrowed his eyes. 'That's *exactly* what I'm worried about.'

Tyler and I followed all the instructions and Tyler didn't even complain that Mr Tull insisted on being there when we were doing the actual soldering (though he did mutter something about having done it more times than most electricians). Once we'd got our wires connected and had made a switch out of two pins, a paper clip and a piece of cardboard, Mr Tull told us we could use some coloured card to make a birthday card with the lights pushed through it. Then he went off to see how Zoe was getting on with her football-themed card (she was putting lights around the goalposts).

As soon as Mr Tull was out of earshot, Tyler turned to me. 'OK, so I've got a better idea.'

'What do you mean?' I felt nervous, but part of me wanted to see what Tyler was thinking. One thing I knew was that it definitely wouldn't be what Mr Tull had in mind.

'Well, a birthday card is OK, but don't you think we should make something a bit more imaginative?'

'Like what?'

Tyler delved under the desk and brought out his bag. He rummaged around in it and took out a long transparent tube. 'A lightsaber for Luke Skywalker! We can put the lights inside and make it a Christmas one – did you notice the lights are white and green? It will be like a seasonal version of his usual one!'

'But where did you get the tube from?'

Tyler gave me a look of pretend surprise. 'Haven't you heard the saying "Always be prepared"?'

I laughed. 'I thought your inventions were to help people. How exactly does a Christmas lightsaber help anyone?'

'Don't you think Luke Skywalker deserves a Christmas present after all he's done for the Rebel Alliance?'

In the end, I got into the spirit by cutting out little Christmas trees to stick onto the handle. It looked epic. When Mr Tull came over to check on our work, he didn't look particularly surprised. 'That's an interesting-looking *card*, guys,' he said. 'Interesting in that it's not *actually* a card, is it?'

'We thought it would make a nice birthday present for someone whose birthday is near Christmas,' Tyler told him.

'So it's *sort of* like a card,' I added. I thought I should support Tyler and try and show Mr Tull we hadn't ignored the instructions completely (though I guess we kind of had).

Mr Tull picked it up and switched it on so that the little white and green bulbs glowed. (It really did look cool.)

'Happy Birthday . . . and Merry Christmas!' Tyler threw his arms in the air.

I saw Mr Tull's mouth twitch and knew we weren't going to get into trouble. 'You know, Tyler, the one thing I can guarantee with you is that I never know what you're going to come up with next.'

'It's true,' Tyler said, nodding seriously. 'I'm full of surprises.'

And I couldn't wait until the next one.

Sandwiches

Even lunchtimes were different with Tyler around. I hadn't noticed what Tyler was eating until one day Zoe stopped at our table as we were taking our lunches out. 'What is it today, Tyler? Cheese and strawberry jam?'

I looked at Tyler's sandwich bag with more interest. 'Cheese and what?'

Zoe reached over and prodded Tyler's bag. 'Tyler doesn't just come up with weird inventions,' she told me. 'He likes to come up with weird sandwich fillings too – weird and *disgusting* fillings.'

'You have no taste,' Tyler said.

'You have no *taste buds*,' Zoe said, walking on to sit next to Dani.

Tyler shook his head sadly. 'It's tragic, really,' he said. 'Zoe's going to sit and have her usual boring egg mayonnaise, while I am enjoying a MasterChef-final-worthy sandwich.'

I peered at it as he took a bite. 'Are those *cornflakes*?'

Tyler nodded, finished chewing and swallowed. 'Yup. Cornflakes, peanut butter and mayonnaise – food of the gods.'

'Cornflakes, peanut butter and mayonnaise,' I repeated. It was the sort of thing I might say to Mum in our Yucky Food Competition.

Tyler laughed at my expression. 'Don't knock it till you try it,' he said, holding out the other half of his sandwich.

'Oh no, you're all right,' I said.

'Go on, what have you got to lose?'

'Uh, the contents of my stomach?'

Tyler kept holding out the sandwich. He had a challenging look in his eye. 'Jack, I promise you, you will not regret this,' he said.

'So *you* say,' I told him. But I gave in and took it. I hadn't known Tyler for long but I already understood that he was what my mum called a Determined Type. I took a bite and chewed.

Tyler watched my face. 'Delicious, right?'

'Actually . . . it's not bad.' It really wasn't. The cornflakes made the sandwich crunchy and the mayonnaise stopped the peanut butter from sticking to the roof of your mouth. It was different, but it was kind of tasty different.

Tyler waved his hand in the air. 'It's a *lot* better than not bad. Wait until you try my Snickers sandwich.'

'What's in that? Chocolate bars?'

'Peanut butter and Nutella.' Tyler started ticking off combinations on his fingers. 'Then when I'm trying to be a bit healthier I'll do hummus, red pepper, spring onion and crushed crackers. Or cream cheese, celery and Hula Hoops.' He looked at me seriously. 'Having something crunchy is very important so you have to remember to add them at the last minute.'

I looked down at my cheese roll and wondered what it would be like with a few cracker crumbs or Hula Hoops in it. That was the thing about Tyler – even *lunch* became something he could turn into a new invention.

Mum's New Occupation

Mum had earned enough from her last reality-TV job (*The Real-Life Cat Stars of Viral Cat Videos*) to mean she didn't have to find a new job straight away, but she wasn't someone who liked hanging around. About a week after I started at School Six, I came home to find her sitting on the sofa, surrounded by the usual assortment of paper, pens and empty mugs, peering at the screen of her laptop as she pecked at the keyboard.

'Find anything?' I asked, removing a cup of tea she'd only half drunk and carrying it to the kitchen counter.

'Not yet.'

Our new house was open-plan, which meant that the kitchen, dining and living areas were all in one big room. Mum had thought this would help her be more organised. What it actually meant was that we no longer had walls between Mum's mess.

I made my way back across to her through the piles of stuff, and looked over her shoulder at her laptop screen.

'Oh good, you can take over and find me something,' Mum said. 'My eyes are going wonky from the small print on this jobs website.'

'No problem,' I told her. 'OK – how about . . . Front of house manager for an Italian restaurant? That would be brilliant – you could get discounts on pizza!'

'I don't want to work nights,' Mum said.

'Customer services phone operative? That sounds good.'

'No, it doesn't. What that really means is "listening to people making complaints all day".' She shuddered. 'No, thanks.'

'French-speaking Sales Executive.'

'I don't speak French.'

I waved her words away. 'You could learn.'

'No.'

'If you're this fussy, it's going to take a while,' I told her. 'You need to see the possibilities!' But she just laughed.

*

In the end, it only took one more day for Mum to find a new job. On Saturday, we had planned to mix job-searching for her with unpacking boxes from the move (along with me finding all the things Mum had unpacked and already lost), but while we were still eating our breakfast, the doorbell rang.

'Will you get it, sweetheart? I haven't had enough tea to face the world yet.'

'That's because you never finish drinking it,' I told her, but I was already moving towards the front door.

'Hi!' A tall man in a check shirt stood on the doorstep beaming at me. 'My name's Francis.' The way he spoke sounded as if he was announcing the winner of the lottery. 'We're neighbours! So I thought I'd pop by with my "Welcome to Hardy Road Pack"!' He held out a large canvas bag that had 'Save the Whales' printed on it.

'Oh, thanks.' I took the bag and looked down at it. It was very heavy.

'It's only a few basics,' Francis said. 'Parmesan cheese, fresh basil, a decent bottle of Chianti, some fresh pappardelle pasta . . . all fresh from the local deli!'

This was definitely a first. Didn't neighbours usually offer tea and sugar?

Mum came up behind me. 'An Italian dinner! How thoughtful! Thank you so much!'

It was like talking in exclamation marks was catching. I moved out of the way so that Francis and my mum could shake hands and beam at each other.

'You're so welcome . . . um . . . ?' Francis hesitated.

'My name's Maggie and this is my son, Jack.'

'I always think that anyone can get tea bags and sugar,' Francis told Mum. 'But when you've moved you usually already have the tea because of the removal guys. And I thought you might not have had a chance to get fresh ingredients in, what with all the unpacking and reorganising. But . . .' His smile suddenly faltered. 'Of course you might not like pasta.'

'We *love* pasta!' Mum took the bag from me. 'It was a very kind thought.'

Francis beamed again. His smile stretched right across his face.

'Would you like a cup of tea or coffee?' Mum pushed me gently aside so that she could welcome Francis in.

'Well, if you're sure it's not too much trouble,' Francis said, following Mum through to the kitchen area. Then he gasped.

I saw Mum turn towards him, confused, but I already knew what he was reacting to. I looked past Francis as he took in our open-plan living area, which had become more like an open-plan *dumping* area since we'd moved in. There were half-unpacked boxes everywhere and trails of clothes and papers winding like paths from the kitchen space to the dining space and on to the living-room space. There were newspapers and piles of post spread across the sofa, and I spotted a mug sitting at the top of the stairs that led up to our bedrooms.

'When did this happen?' Francis gasped. 'What an awful start to your new life here! I hope the police catch the people who did it!'

'What?' Mum looked from Francis to me. 'Sorry – police?'

'We haven't been burgled,' I said to Francis. 'We've just been . . . unpacking.'

Francis flushed the deepest red I've ever seen. 'Oh! I'm so sorry! I'm so rude! I thought –'

'We'd been visited by thieves?' Mum asked, her mouth twitching. 'Well, unless Jack has the chance to clean up after me, then they'd have a job finding anything worth stealing in this mess.' Then she erupted into a giggle. 'Jack, I don't think "cleaner" – or anything involving tidiness – is going to work for my new occupation.'

Then she started laughing properly as Francis looked even more confused.

'I think you'd better come in,' she told him, shifting some papers on the floor with her foot so he could get by.

Later, after we'd all had something to drink, I left them to it and went upstairs. When I came back down, Francis had gone and Mum was doing a celebratory jive dance around the living room (or at least around the bits of floor that were still visible).

'What's up?' I asked.

'I've got a job!' Mum said triumphantly. 'I think Francis felt so bad about insulting my housekeeping skills that he felt he should do something to make up for it.'

'So he gave you a *job*? That's quite a big apology,' I said.

Mum laughed. 'It turns out that Francis runs a care home in the area and they need a new manager. He said they're in crisis mode because the last manager walked out without giving proper notice. I explained what I used to do, and he hired me as an administrator on the spot, said we could have a two-week trial and see how we go.'

'Wow. Congratulations,' I told her. I remembered how she had said on Moving Day that this time we were going to stay in one place. Maybe she'd been right.

Annoying Things

One of the things I now knew about Tyler was that he liked starting discussions. He'd set off a question like a match to a bunch of dry twigs. On the Tuesday of my second week of school, when Mr Tull went to get some books from the stockroom and left us to work on his latest worksheet about Greek myths and how the Romans had nicked most of their gods, Tyler decided to start up a new topic.

'Tell me something that gets on your nerves,' he said.

I frowned at him. 'Are you just trying to bring up SnarkyMark?' (I'd admitted to him earlier that I *was* really tired of SnarkyMark. I hadn't meant to, but something about Tyler meant that I kept letting out secrets.)

Tyler started laughing. 'No, not like something you *hate*, just something that annoys you a bit.'

'Isn't that the same thing?'

'Of course not.' He pulled out something from his pencil case. 'Like, my sister Abby is always losing stuff, especially if it's small. She finds that very annoying, but she doesn't *hate* it. Anyway, I fixed her problem.' He held up a green rubber which had been fitted to the side of a sharpener. 'I call it the Sharber,' Tyler said. 'Only one thing to lose instead of two! Plus it's bigger, so she probably won't lose it anyway.'

'Clever,' I said. I thought of all the times Mum put down a pen, or her glasses, or, yeah, a rubber, and then couldn't find them. Combining things did mean fewer things to lose. Mind you, glasses and car keys were the two things Mum lost all the time, and I didn't see gluing *them* together working too well.

'So –' Tyler tapped the Sharber on the table – 'what do you find annoying?'

I nearly came out with my standard, 'I don't know really.' That was what I'd say if I was following Sherlock code. But before I knew what I was doing, I found myself opening my mouth. 'I hate it when you get a school trip to somewhere good or do something else that's fun and then the teachers make you come back and write about it.'

Tyler laughed. 'Excellent one!' He turned to Zoe. 'What do you find annoying?'

Zoe gave him a hard stare. 'You.'

Another thing I'd learned about Tyler is that he wasn't easily put off. 'Apart from me,' he urged her.

'When they only allow you two footballs at break and your friend kicks them both onto the roof in the first five minutes,' said Zoe, switching her glare to Dani.

'It was an accident!' Dani said.

'My one is when you've got something to look forward to and time slows down,' Tyler said. 'You know, like one human year is seven dog years or whatever. It's the same. One day feels like a month when you're waiting for something you're looking forward to doing.'

'Tyler, you know that time doesn't actually slow down, right?' Zoe said.

'Yeah, but it *feels* like it does,' Tyler said. 'So it's true really.'

Zoe shook her head and made an I-give-up face, but I knew exactly what Tyler meant.

'I know what you mean, Ty,' said Isaac, who had come over. 'It's like when you're waiting for the new SnarkyMark post and he says he'll put it up at seven o'clock on a Tuesday, yeah? And it's like five o'clock and it feels like seven is like *next year*.'

Tyler gave me a half-wink and I tried not to smile.

'I've got one,' James said. 'When teachers ban a

game because they think it sounds violent even when it isn't. I *really* miss Zombie Apocalypse . . .'

And then we were off, everyone chatting and laughing and coming up with more and more examples. I watched as Tyler encouraged everyone to keep going, nodding and laughing, and I realised that Tyler reminded me of my dad. Somehow he could make ordinary days brighter and more fun than anyone else could.

Settling In

It turned out Mum had to go into Trouble Ninja mode straight away at her new job. Apparently the state of the computers and the paperwork was so bad that it was going to take her at least two weeks to sort it all out. Mum was delighted – she loved having a crisis to deal with – and Francis was delighted to have someone come in and solve all the problems. It was more than that though. Mum said that Francis was a great boss and she loved the people living at the home.

'You'll have to meet Mr Gray,' she told me the evening of her second day. 'He's a retired musician, and though he can't play piano any more because of his arthritis, he sings every morning while he's getting dressed. He likes Taylor Swift – and he even does a bit of rap. It's a much better way to start the day than being yelled at down my mobile because the production's behind schedule and might go over budget.'

Mum liked Francis too. He was cheerful and smiley and within a week had decided that Mum was the best thing that had ever happened to his business. He gave her a raise and an extra week of holiday entitlement. 'Not that I know when I'm going to be able to take it,' Mum laughed. 'I can't go anywhere before I've got things straight, and everything in that office is as knotted as a knitter's bag of wool.' She didn't sound upset about it though, or even particularly stressed, and even though she was in Trouble Ninja mode, I could see that she was happy. Happier than I'd seen her since Dad left.

In the Wild

At the beginning of the next week, Mr Tull gave us a letter about a nature walk on Friday. 'You'll need walking shoes or wellies, a raincoat, a packed lunch and a bottle of water,' he told us. 'Extra items are not necessary,' he added, looking at Tyler as usual.

'But we'll be in the wild, sir,' Tyler said, his eyebrows lifted in mock horror. 'What are we supposed to do if we meet a wild pig? Or an angry bull? Or a charging chicken? We'll need things to protect us.'

'I don't think that's likely, Tyler,' Mr Tull said, 'given that the point of our walk is to identify plants and insects and we won't be anywhere near a farm. But I'm sure Jack will be happy to protect you.' He smiled at me.

I smiled back. There was something nice about the way Mr Tull seemed to think Tyler and I were becoming good friends. It meant that maybe it was true.

*

On the walk we had a worksheet to fill out. It had pictures of different plants, trees and insects to look for. As we walked along the path in a long line, it turned out Zoe knew as much about insects as Isaac and Libby knew about SnarkyMark. By the end of the first ten minutes of the walk, she'd already pointed out a stag beetle, a dragonfly and a flying ant.

'Nice work, Zoe,' Tyler told her after she'd spotted the ant and we'd ticked it off on our worksheets. 'At this rate we'll be finished in no time!'

'Don't let her do *all* the work, Tyler,' Mr Tull told him as he came up behind us.

'I don't mind, sir,' Zoe said. 'It's nice to show Tyler that he doesn't know as much as he thinks he does.'

'Oi! My brain is stuffed full of more facts than you've had hot dinners.'

Zoe tapped her forehead. 'Not about insects it isn't. My mum says I'm as good as a proper entomologist. And I bet you don't even know what an entomologist *is*.'

'Someone who studies insects,' Mr Tull said, putting one hand on Zoe's shoulder and one hand on Tyler's. 'Now, if you don't mind, let's have a bit less arguing and more actual entomology, all right?'

Tyler took a breath to argue (I'd noticed he liked to have the last word) when we heard a loud shout up ahead.

Tyler and I ran along with Mr Tull to see what had happened and saw Isaac standing stock still on the path, looking shaken, his arm outstretched.

'What's wrong, Isaac?' Mr Tull looked in the direction Isaac was pointing.

'It's a *monster*!'

We all stared at the path until we saw the very large spider Isaac was staring at.

'It's a spider, Isaac, nothing to be frightened of,' Mr Tull told him. 'There are no poisonous spiders around here.'

'I heard that thing's *footsteps*. I think it's got its own *shoes*,' Isaac said.

'Oooh, that's a tube web spider!' Zoe had caught up with us and was peering at it with interest. 'They make tubes out of their silk to hide in.'

Isaac looked a bit sick. 'Well, I wish he'd hide in his stupid tube now!'

'Oh no,' Zoe told him. 'It's definitely not a he. Only the females get big like that.' She looked over at Tyler as if to say, *See?*

'SnarkyMark hates spiders too,' Libby told Isaac.

'Do you remember that post he did about them? Hilarious.'

'Yeah, Libs. The thing is, right now I don't really care,' Isaac told her.

Libby looked shocked. Not wanting to talk about SnarkyMark meant it was a serious situation.

'Just walk on past it. It won't hurt you.' I could see that Mr Tull was trying not to smile.

'I can't go past it! It might attack me!'

'It's all right, Isaac, Jack and I will take care of it,' Tyler said in a voice that sounded a bit like he'd cast himself as a superhero.

We would?

Tyler whipped off his backpack and pulled out a long stick with what looked like a nutcracker taped to the end. Then he took out an empty jam jar and unscrewed the lid.

'Jack, can you hold the jar open, then stand ready?'

'Uh, sure.' I took the jar. I felt like a magician's assistant or something.

Tyler moved softly towards the spider, pressing on a lever near the top of the stick, which made the nutcracker at the other end open and close. He positioned the stick over the spider and then clamped down on the lever, catching the creature in between the jaws of the nutcracker. 'Got it!' He swung the stick over towards me. 'OK, Jack, stand by!'

I held the jar out as far as I could (I wasn't frightened of spiders but I didn't exactly want to encourage it to walk up my arm) and he dropped it in. Everyone clapped as I slammed the lid on the top.

Tyler patted his stick. 'That's the successful launch of the Multi Legs Catcher complete then.'

'Why didn't you drop it somewhere else?' Isaac asked. 'I mean, that's gross,' he said, pointing at the spider racing from one side of the jar to the other.

'Because now we can see if Zoe is right about which kind of spider it is and tick it off on the worksheet,' Tyler said. 'Didn't you notice there was more than one spider species we had to spot?'

'You don't actually need to check because I'm right,' Zoe said. 'But you know, if you want to look like an idiot . . .'

Tyler and Zoe stuck out their tongues at each other but then they both laughed. It was obvious that although they argued a lot, they were actually pretty good friends.

'Well, for once, Tyler, an invention of yours has helped us achieve some work,' Mr Tull told him. 'Instead of *disrupting* us, which is more usual.'

'I knew we'd need some extra accessories,' Tyler said happily. 'Thanks for the help, Jack. Good thing you're calm in a crisis.'

I wasn't sure helping put a spider in a jam jar counted as dealing with a crisis, but I was still pleased. Maybe I had a bit of Mum's Trouble Ninja talent. I could definitely use it.

Different Kinds of Mess

For ages Dad loved all the stories about Mum's job. He was proud of her when she went into Trouble Ninja mode, and used to demand the latest 'episode', laughing along as she turned it into a brilliant story. He brought her treats when she got fed up and tidied up after her the way I do now.

But when he started studying again, things changed. Stacks of books and papers appeared and Dad had dark shadows under his eyes from staying up late to study. He was less happy about me wanting to play 'Bear' (a game we'd invented where I flung myself onto him from the sofa or armchairs, roaring), because sometimes I'd accidentally knock into his folders and mess up his work. When I suggested things to do, instead of 'Sure' or 'Why not?', he'd say 'Maybe in a bit,' and 'Not now, buddy'.

It wasn't just me that Dad was more impatient with. He got grumpy about Mum having to work such long hours. Late at night, when they thought I was asleep in bed, I'd hear raised voices snaking up from under the kitchen door.

I started to feel nervous in the evening if Mum hadn't appeared by the time dinner was ready. I'd try and distract Dad by telling him stories of my own, but my stories didn't seem to make him laugh and I couldn't keep his attention any more. After a while he'd snap at me to, 'Please shush now, Jack.' He seemed to have used up all the patience he had when I was little. Or maybe I'd stopped being fun to be around.

Then Mum and Dad stopped waiting until I was asleep to fight and it felt like it wasn't only Mum who made a mess. It was the two of them and the tangle of ugly words between them. And eventually I'd realised they might not be able to clean it up.

Favourite Colours

Altogether, Move Six wasn't going the way our moves usually did. For one thing, I'd definitely never come home to the smell of fresh paint. But on the Tuesday of our third week, I walked through the front door to find Mum painting the kitchen. Mum had never had time to fix things up before. She'd sometimes talked about it, but it was usually while she was flicking through a magazine at the dentist's. It never came to anything.

After we'd left our old house, we lived in some places where it might have been better if they hadn't had time to decorate. There was the Thomas the Tank Engine wallpaper in both bedrooms in Move Three, the dark grey kitchen and bright red bedrooms in Move Two and wall-to-wall neon purple in Move Four (no, no, no, no, no). Mostly I'd learned to 'unsee' bad decoration, and if it ever got to me, I'd remind myself that we'd be leaving soon, because we always did.

So even though things seemed to be going smoothly so far, I was still surprised to see Mum painting the kitchen area a soft shade of yellow.

'What do you think?' Mum asked me, stepping down off the mini-stepladder.

'It's great. Big improvement.'

'I think I'll use this colour for all of the open-plan area and then maybe white for the downstairs loo?'

'Right.'

'And then we'll choose which colour you want for your bedroom. I'm thinking a pale kind of misty green for mine. I've always wanted a green bedroom.'

I filled the kettle and switched it on. It was weird hearing Mum plan ahead and talk about painting and colours as if we were going to be here for long enough to make it worth the effort.

'Here, I got you these to look through. Any idea what you think you'll go for? What's your favourite colour these days?' She handed me a pile of colour charts from different paint companies and I looked down at the tiny squares of colour, then back at Mum, who was smiling at me, her forehead smooth instead of creased in her usual frown of worry and concentration.

'I don't know,' I said. I finished making the tea and passed Mum a cup. 'I think I'll go and get changed.'

'All right then, sweetheart,' Mum said. 'But have a think about colours – I want to get this all done as soon as I can!'

I took my tea and went upstairs. If we really were going to stick around this time I had a new kind of problem to handle. Not only did I have to work out what my favourite colour actually was, I also had to figure out exactly who I was going to be.

The Visit

One weekend, about a year after Dad left, he came to take me out for the day. He'd done that most weekends since leaving, but he'd said the week before that he might not be able to see me as regularly because he'd been offered a new job a few hundred miles away. He'd looked really upset when he told me, but I couldn't help wondering why he'd had to get a job so far from us. Mum had said it was because he was starting a new career and didn't have much experience yet, but sometimes late at night I thought there might be another reason. It might be because when he did come to see me, I wasn't saying and doing the right things.

I'd been so excited about seeing him that I couldn't sleep the night before. But then when he was there on our doorstep I was awkward, nervous and embarrassed. I felt the way you might if you turned up at someone's party in fancy dress and found everyone else was in normal clothes.

'Hey, buddy,' Dad said, looking past me at Mum, who was standing just behind me.

'You'll have him back by six?'

I didn't have to look to know that Mum had her Trouble Ninja expression on.

'I thought maybe I could take you both out for dinner when I bring him back.' Dad gave Mum a hopeful look. I saw that he hadn't shaved and that he had dark rings under his eyes.

'I don't think that would be a good idea,' Mum said, her voice flat, not meeting his eyes. 'I'll see you at six, Jack.' Then she squeezed my shoulder and walked away down the hall. 'Don't forget his jacket,' she called behind her.

'I do still remember how to be his parent, you know!' Dad shouted. Then he jerked his head towards the street. 'Come on, Jack, let's go.'

He'd forgotten to pick up my jacket, so I grabbed it before I closed the door.

We went to the park and sat by the pond. Dad asked me what I wanted to do and I shrugged. He bought me an ice cream that I didn't really feel like. I ate it too fast and it gave me brain freeze. Dad kept asking me the same questions – how was school, how was Mum, how was I – and I kept giving him the same answer. Fine. I tried to sound as if I meant it, because I could see he was miserable and I wanted him to feel better. But the more I said it, the more miserable he sounded. I realised I was making him feel worse. Then I wondered if he wanted to be here at all. Maybe he was fed up with me. Maybe he wanted the visit to be over. Maybe he couldn't wait to be off to start his new life. I told him I didn't feel well and he asked if I wanted to go back early. I said yes.

I haven't seen him since.

Things Get Tricky

The twins caught up with me outside the school gates. Since I'd gone round to their house we'd had a few SnarkyMark conversations at break times ('Hilarious'), but I'd avoided the subject of Project Moneybags.

'Hey, Jack,' Isaac said. 'How's it going?'

'All right,' I said.

'You're getting on well with Ty,' Libby said.

'Yeah, you two are like this.' Isaac crossed his fingers and held them up. 'Good work.'

I scuffed my toe into the pavement. I didn't like them making it sound as if I was some kind of spy.

'You talked to him about the plan yet?' Libby asked.

'Um, not yet,' I said.

'Biding your time, yeah?' Isaac said. 'No worries. But look, what we thought was, if you can get us one of Ty's inventions, we could get it up on our website and show him what we can do. Prove we're the best.'

Libby nodded.

'I can ask him,' I said. I realised I didn't have a choice now. Not that it mattered – I was sure Tyler would say no and then that would be the end of it.

Isaac and Libby looked at each other.

'See,' Isaac said, 'what we were thinking is maybe we could make it a surprise, yeah?'

'Like you could maybe *borrow* something to give to us,' Libby said.

'Then we could show him what it could look like, you know, on our website.'

'You've got a website now?' Somehow I hadn't expected Isaac and Libby's plans to come to anything so, well, real.

'Yeah, our older brother did it for us,' Isaac said. 'He's doing business at college. And he's like a founding partner in Project Moneybags.'

'Right,' I said. 'But I don't know . . .'

'Look,' Isaac said, coming closer and putting his arm around my shoulder. 'We're trying to *help* Ty, you know.'

'Like, if he sells this stuff, he can get what he needs to make more stuff,' Libby said.

I didn't say much, but I think they thought that meant I agreed. That's the problem with using Sherlock code – everyone thinks you'll go along with anything they say. The thing was, this time I didn't know if I would.

Tyler's House

The next morning, Tyler invited me to go back with him after school the following day to see some of his inventions. I said yes, thinking that I could tell him about Isaac and Libby while I was there. I was pretty sure that when they said 'borrow' they pretty much meant 'steal', and there was no way I was going to do that. I'd tell him what they wanted to do and leave it up to him.

When we arrived Tyler led us straight into the kitchen, where his dad was reading the paper and drinking a mug of something that smelled really odd.

'Tyler,' he said, 'maybe *you* can convince your mum that drinking this . . . *potion*, or possibly *poison* –' he pointed at the mug, making a face – 'is *not* going to do me any good.'

'Mum says it will help your blood pressure and she's

a nurse,' Tyler told him, shrugging his bag onto the table. 'Drink it.' He gestured towards me. 'Dad, this is Jack.'

Tyler's dad waved at me. 'Hello, Jack, nice to meet you.'

I waved back.

'My family likes to make my life a misery,' Tyler's dad told me, 'under the guise of improving my health. Tyler here has even cut down my salt intake by using one of those infernal inventions of his.'

Tyler brightened. 'Oh yeah! My Saltsealer!' He pointed to a stainless-steel cylinder on a sideboard. 'It will only let out a certain amount,' he said. 'It stops Dad from having too much salt because that's not good for his blood pressure.'

'It stops my food tasting of anything,' Tyler's dad grumbled. But I could tell he didn't really mind, because when Tyler went closer he reached up to ruffle his hair. I had a sudden memory of Dad doing the same thing. I blinked hard and picked up the Saltsealer to get a better look.

'Come on, Jack,' Tyler said. 'Mum's still at work, so you've only got to meet my sister and then I can take you to the operations room.'

'Whoa, you *are* privileged!' Tyler's dad smiled at me.

'Not very many people get invited there.'

'That's because *some* people don't know how to follow simple rules,' Tyler said, raising his eyebrows at his dad.

'I don't know.' Tyler's dad shrugged. 'One *tiny* little accident with a work in progress and you're never allowed to forget it.'

'He set me back days on my Picky Eater Picker Tongs,' Tyler said. 'He thought it was a normal set of barbecue tongs and melted the ends.'

'A tragedy that still haunts my dreams,' Tyler's dad said, winking at me.

Then Tyler took me into a living room which had enough books to stock a library or bookshop. There were books on the shelves that lined the walls, and piles on the floor and more piles on every piece of furniture. The sofa was so covered in books it was hard to see how anyone could actually sit down.

'Hey, Abby,' Tyler called.

A head emerged from behind an armchair that was facing away from us, towards one of the windows. A girl knelt up in the chair, her arms crossed over the back of it.

'Hey,' she said. 'Umba coo?'

Tyler shrugged. 'Berko my.'

Abby saw my expression. 'We made up our own language when we were little,' she explained, smiling at me. 'And it kind of stuck.'

It looked as if Tyler came from a family of inventors.

'Yeah, it's useful when we don't want Mum and Dad to know what we're talking about,' Tyler said. 'And the bonus is that it drives them up the wall.'

Abby laughed. 'Just for that it's worth the effort of remembering it.'

'This is Jack,' Tyler told her. 'He's new at school. I'm going to show him the operations room.'

'Don't talk his ears off, Tyler, or decide that he has to see *everything*, or he'll be in there until Christmas,' Abby said. She looked at me. 'I hope you're ready for this.'

I followed Tyler out of the room, thinking that, for once, I definitely was.

The Room
Where It Happens

The operations room was right at the back of the house with a huge window and a couple of skylights. Along one wall were pulleys attached to shelves so that you could move them up and down. Opposite was a long table with rows and rows of tools of every type (not that I knew what any of them were apart from the hammers, screwdrivers and spanners). It wasn't just the tables and shelves that were heaped with things though – the floor was littered with objects of all sizes, from yogurt cartons to big steel canisters to rolls of copper wire. 'This is all yours?'

'Yeah,' Tyler said, walking over to the table. 'I get most of it at jumble sales, car-boot sales and off eBay. And I'm friends with some guys down the dump and at our local garage. They give me stuff they don't need

that's going to the scrap yard.' He pointed to another long table at the end of the room which was loaded up with what looked like an old car bumper and lots of scrap metal. There was also a battered guitar with a piece of string trailing from it. A drumstick was tied mid-way along the string.

'Do you play?' I pointed at the guitar.

'Nope,' Tyler said. 'That's the Waker-Upper – one of my earliest inventions.' He picked up the guitar and took it to the door, attaching the string to a nearby hook. Then he positioned the drumstick that was tied to the string over the guitar. 'See, when your mum or dad opens the door to call you, the stick falls on the strings of the guitar and wakes you up.' He demonstrated, opening the door. Sure enough, the drumstick fell on

the strings and made a twanging noise.

'But why wouldn't you just use an alarm? Or wait for them to wake you up if they're coming in to see you anyway?'

Tyler looked up to the ceiling and sighed deeply as if I had spectacularly missed the point. 'First of all, alarm clocks sound evil,' he said. 'Second of all, wouldn't you rather be woken up by the gentle twang of guitar strings instead of a grumpy grown-up saying you have five minutes to get dressed, brush your teeth and be at the breakfast table?'

He had a point.

'So this room is just for your inventions?'

'Yep. This is where the magic happens.' Tyler looked around proudly.

'Are you going to show me some more stuff then?'

'Thought you'd never ask.' Tyler leaned backwards and tugged on a red cord that was dangling near him. There was a rattling sound and a hatch opened in the ceiling and a tray descended (a bit jerkily) down to us. On it was a Tupperware container of biscuits and a flask with two plastic cups.

'Ceiling Service for snacks,' Tyler said, looking pleased. 'Help yourself.'

'Um, thanks,' I said, taking a cup and pouring out orange squash from the flask.

'See, this way I can get something to eat without having to go to the kitchen when I'm working on an invention or disturbing Dad when he's making dinner,' Tyler said. 'And it's in the roof space so nothing gets dusty even if I'm making lots of mess.'

'It's great. What else do you have up there? Blankets? A TV?'

He took a biscuit out of the Tupperware and looked thoughtful. 'No, but you're right. Why not? I mean, you could have a completely clear room and have everything descend when you needed it, couldn't you?'

'A bed,' I said. 'And a table and chairs in the dining room.'

'Exactly!' He pointed at me. 'You know, you're very handy to have around.'

'I am?'

'Yeah, that's not the first time you've given me an idea. You're turning into a very useful friend.' Tyler studied me, smiling. 'Plus you're not a bad listener.'

'And you like talking.'

'Well, *yeah*!'

I laughed and then looked back at the Ceiling Service tray. 'Maybe you could have a tray of night stuff that came down over the bed too,' I said. 'The book you're reading, a night light that you're always losing because it's so small . . .'

'Is this for you?'

'Not me, my mum,' I said. 'She loses *everything*. I've seen her lose a freshly made *sandwich*.'

'Right. So she needs my help,' Tyler said.

'She probably does.'

'OK,' Tyler said cheerfully. 'I'll see what I can come up with. I like a challenge.' He got up and took a notepad and a pencil from the table piled high with tools. 'First what I have to do is write down everything the invention has to solve,' he told me, 'That way I don't get distracted. I make a full list of all the problems and then do a mind map to help me come up with ways to solve them.' He held up an example. A mind map seemed to be a big circle in the middle of a sheet of paper with a word in it and lots of other bubbles coming out with other words in them all around it.

'On your mind map, are you completely lost?' I froze for a split second as soon as I said it. I'd done it again – said the first thing that came to mind instead of following Sherlock code and keeping my mouth shut. But Tyler was grinning. He didn't seem to mind. It was weird. The only person I'd normally joke around with like this was Mum. And even though Tyler wasn't a safe friend according to Sherlock code, I was realising that that's what he made me feel: safe. Safe to say what I thought, safe to joke around, safe to relax.

'A mind map, since you clearly don't have a clue,' Tyler said, 'is where you put down all the ideas you have without thinking them through – even if they seem bonkers – and then you see where they lead you. So, what shall we put first?'

I realised that Tyler was serious. He was going to spend time coming up with something for my mum to use, something to help her. Which meant that he thought it was worth doing.

'Thanks,' I told him. 'This is really nice of you.'

'What are friends for?' Tyler shrugged and started

scribbling on his notebook, not waiting for an answer.

It was just as well because I didn't know what to say.

'Don't worry,' Tyler said. 'Once I've finished my new invention, your mum will never lose anything again.'

That morning I'd had to help Mum find her facecloth (it was on top of the kettle after she'd used it instead of a dish towel) and her glasses (in the bread bin – no idea why). I laughed. 'If you manage that, then you really are a genius,' I told him.

Tyler gave me a mock serious look. 'That, Jack, is already an established fact,' he said.

Mum on the Home Front

Instead of charging around all the time and having her phone glued to her ear day and night, or dashing out to solve the latest crisis, Mum had started coming home at the same time every day and doing something around the house. I came home from school a couple of days after my visit to Tyler's house and the whole living room was clear. Since it had been full of boxes when I left that morning, I was a bit panicked. Maybe this time we really had been burgled? Then Mum appeared with her arms full of cushions.

'You've been unpacking?' Mum wasn't known for unpacking. Or at least, not for unpacking things and actually putting them away. When Mum unpacked, there was usually a trail across the room marking the spot from where she'd walked to all the places she went along the way. I looked around and wondered if she'd hidden things under the chairs.

'Yes, isn't it great?' She scattered the cushions on the sofa and stood back to admire them. It looked good, but weird, as if it was someone else's house. We weren't normally around for long enough to even take the cushions out of their boxes, let alone arrange them.

Mum leaned forward to give a throw on the sofa a final tweak. 'Now that I've got a job where I actually finish on time, I've got time to decorate, fix things, cook, and, well, *be around*.'

When Mum worked on the television programmes, she didn't have set hours; she was just 'working'. All the time. If you think about it, it was kind of a miracle that she managed to unpack anything at all back then.

'I'm not sure that's good news about the cooking,' I said.

'Oi!' Mum picked up one of the cushions and flung it at me.

'No, it's great though.' I said. 'I mean that you'll be around more.'

Mum went still and her eyes filled up. 'Oh, Jack . . . I know it's been hard for you. But you've always been so good about all our moves and me being out so much.'

'It's been fine, honestly.' I had to make sure Mum didn't feel bad.

'You've coped so well with it all. You've been so grown-up.' Mum smiled, but her eyes were still shiny. 'Anyway –' she blinked hard – 'I think you should be congratulating me on the grand job I've done unpacking.'

'Let me see where you've put everything first,' I said, glad to be able to lighten the tone. I didn't want to talk about how bad Mum felt that we'd moved around so much, or how 'good' I'd been about it. It made me think about Dad leaving. And how I'd been one of the reasons why.

Shipwrecked!

In our next literacy lesson Mr Tull said we were going to write a short play in pairs about being washed up on an island after a storm. 'One of you will be the leader,' he said, 'and the other person will follow along at first, but then decide that they should be the leader instead. And I want that person not to speak but to show everything they're feeling through their expressions and gestures. You can make it funny or you can make it serious – I don't mind.'

Tyler bounced up and down on his heels (today he was wearing a pair of trainers with Blu Tack stuck all over them – Tyler insisted that Blu Tack was one of the most useful materials in the entire world). 'Which part do you want, Jack? Speaking or not speaking?' he said. 'I don't care as long as I'm in charge of inventing all the things we'll need to survive on the island. Maybe I should be the one not speaking so I can act out making stuff.'

'Yeah, right, like you could stay quiet for more than a minute,' Zoe said as she picked up her pen to start work.

I was about to answer when Mr Tull stepped forward. 'Actually, I'd like Jack to do the non-speaking part.'

I looked at Mr Tull, surprised, but he just smiled as if he knew something I didn't.

We wrote our script in twenty minutes (having one non-speaking part made it pretty easy) and then we all went off to different parts of the school to rehearse before coming back to present our scenes to the class. Tyler and I ran through our script in the hall – we'd decided to make it funny so I made all my reactions completely over the top. I did a tragic face as we arrived on the island and lots of 'You think so?' faces as Tyler outlined what he'd be making and told me what I should be doing. Then when Tyler told me to come and see the shelter he'd (mimed) built, I took one look and gestured that it was rubbish. ('That's the most unbelievable bit of the script,' Tyler said. 'My shelter would be brilliant.') Finally I started doing King Kong chest-thumping to show I thought I should be leader. It was a bit bonkers, but it was a lot of fun and I decided I might as well throw everything I had into it. It wasn't like I had to say anything, and somehow that made it easier for me. It was a bit like being at home with Mum when we were messing about.

Mum and I have always played that game where you try to make the other person laugh without laughing yourself, so I've had lots of practice at keeping a straight face. Even though Tyler kept cracking up while we ran through it, I managed to not laugh once. When we'd finished, he gave me an approving nod. 'I've discovered your secret talent, Jack,' he said.

'What do you mean?'

Tyler shook his head. 'If you don't know, I'm not telling.' He wouldn't say any more, so we rehearsed a couple more times and then went back to the class.

When it was our turn to perform I felt a bit nervous and thought maybe I should tone my expressions down so I didn't look too silly. But then two things happened. Tyler whispered to me, 'Do it exactly like you did in the hall and it will be great,' and I looked up and caught Mr Tull's eye and he gave me a nod, smiling, as if he was giving me permission for something.

We did it just like before, and everyone laughed, really hard. And you could tell that they weren't laughing *at* us; they were laughing because they thought we were funny.

Mr Tull came up to us, still clapping. 'As I suspected, Jack,' he said. 'You're a natural performer. Excellent facial expressions – very funny.'

Tyler slapped my arm. 'Yeah, you were great. You're as talented with your face as I am with my inventions. Well, almost.'

Mr Tull smiled at me. 'You look like you still need convincing, Jack. Didn't you know you were good at this kind of thing?'

I suppose if I'd thought about it, I could have figured out that I might be OK at performing – after all, every time Mum and I had moved I'd become a whole different person. But I just shrugged a bit and smiled back. 'Thanks.' The thing that was different was that today I'd been me – and people had liked it. From now on all I had to do was make sure that the bits of me I showed were the bits of me they liked.

Tyler's Gifts

A couple of days later, Tyler came into school with an even bigger grin on his face than normal. 'I've done it!' he announced, sinking into his seat.

'Done what?'

'Solved all your mum's problems.'

I raised my eyebrows at him. 'Really? All of them?

'All right, *a lot* of her problems,' he said. 'I've made her some stuff. So when can I come round?'

It was completely against Sherlock code to have anyone back to my house. But then knowing Tyler in the first place was pretty much against the code too. I decided to give in.

'I can't wait to meet Tyler,' Mum told me after I'd asked her if it was OK for him to come over. 'You've never really wanted to invite any friends home before, have you?'

This was her not very subtle way of trying to get me to talk. I knew she used to worry about how few friends I seemed to have. But it wasn't so much that I didn't have them, more that I was careful not to let them get close. Basically, for them not to be *proper* friends. Because what was the point? I was only going to leave again.

I couldn't tell Mum any of that though. So I just shrugged. 'I was thinking that maybe we could have potatoes with jam then mushroom ice cream for tea,' I said. 'Maybe with some shredded boiled cabbage as a starter.'

Mum gave me a hard stare, as if she could tell I was trying to change the subject. Then she smiled. 'Oh, I think we can do better than that – how about salmon-and-chicken-liver cake with caramel-and-blue-cheese sauce?'

I smiled back at her. 'Perfect. Tyler will love it.'

New Inventions

The next morning Tyler arrived at school dragging a big wheelie suitcase.

'Exactly how many things have you made?' I said.

Tyler spread out his hands. 'True genius cannot be restrained,' he said. 'When true genius is set free, there are no limits to its imagination and its power to prove itself.'

'Riiiight.'

Tyler shook his head. 'It's sad to see such cynicism in someone so young . . .'

Mr Tull appeared behind Tyler. 'I'll tell you what, Tyler, I may be *old* and cynical, but it's going to take a lot more than "true genius" to get you through the spelling test on Friday, so I hope at least one of your inventions helps you to knuckle down to remembering the words I set.'

I couldn't help laughing as I saw Tyler's face crumple up in disgust. 'I'm going to invent something for people who can't spell,' he said.

'They already did,' I told him. 'It's called spellcheck.' For a second I worried that he wouldn't like me making fun of him. But Tyler was laughing when he punched my arm.

Isaac and Libby came up to me when Tyler was fetching something for Mr Tull from the stockroom.

'So we heard Tyler's going back to yours today,' Isaac said.

'Yeah.'

Libby nodded. 'And you've got him to bring round some of his stuff. Nice one.'

I still hadn't got round to telling Tyler about their plan or telling Isaac and Libby that I was definitely not 'borrowing' anything from him. I didn't know how any of them would react, so I'd played it safe and stayed quiet. A niggling feeling made me wonder if I'd done the right thing.

'Think of how good it will be when Project Moneybags takes off,' Isaac said. 'We could become famous – like celebrity inventors.'

'They might make a programme about us,' Libby

said. '*Britain's Got Inventors.*'

'*Strictly Inventors,*' Isaac said.

'*The Invent-Off.*'

Isaac and Libby laughed but I wondered why they were putting an 's' on 'inventor'. Tyler was the inventor, not us.

'Once we're up and running,' Isaac told me, 'our brother says we could set up our own YouTube channel, showing Tyler at work. Our brother says people like seeing stuff being made, because that makes it special. He reckons people pay a lot more if things are handmade.'

'And what about the T-shirt idea? Tell him about that,' Libby said.

'Oh yeah,' Isaac said. 'Our brother's got this whole idea for merchandise – that's like T-shirts and bags and stuff like that – once people start buying Tyler's inventions off the website. He says once you've got merch then you can make serious money.'

'Serious,' Libby agreed.

I opened my mouth to say something – this was all getting out of hand. They were assuming that Tyler would be up for helping them make loads of money. But before I could speak, the door opened and Zoe walked in. Isaac slapped me lightly on the back before they backed away to their own seats. 'Get something good, yeah?'

'What was *that* about?' Zoe asked me.

'Nothing,' I said. I hoped I wasn't lying.

When we arrived home after school, Mum came through the kitchen and her eyes widened at the sight of Tyler's wheelie case. 'Goodness, what have you got there?'

Tyler put the suitcase down and came over to shake hands. (Mum looked pretty shocked about that too.)

'Great to meet you,' he said. 'Don't worry, I'm not moving in or anything. I've just brought a few gifts for you.'

'Gifts!' Now she looked really alarmed.

'It's only stuff he's made out of junk,' I told her.

'They're not made out of junk!' Tyler said. 'They're made out of finds and upcycled materials.'

'Yeah, junk, like I said.'

Tyler shook his head at me, but he was smiling.

'Well, whatever they're made of, there seem to be a lot of them,' Mum said, still looking concerned. I knew she was wondering where it would all go.

'It's all useful stuff,' Tyler assured her.

Mum didn't look convinced as he moved further into

the kitchen, dragging the suitcase behind him. 'This suitcase doesn't only have wheels; it has a special steering system,' he explained as he manoeuvred the case into the living-room area.

'Really?' Mum glanced over at me, her eyebrows quirked up in amusement. 'And you came up with that, did you?' She was smiling now, and I breathed out a small sigh of relief. I could tell she liked him.

'Oh yes,' Tyler said. 'The wheels were hopeless before – they were set so deep in the bottom that you could barely move the case. I replaced them with some wheels from my old toy racing cars.'

He brought the suitcase over to the table. 'Is it OK if I set everything up here?'

'Oh! Well, of course, help yourself,' Mum said. 'Would you like a hand?'

'No, no,' Tyler said. 'I want it to be a nice surprise.'

Mum leaned in towards me. 'He's great,' she whispered, in the tone of someone who had made up her mind.

'Yeah,' I whispered back. 'He is.'

Tyler had put the suitcase on the table and now he flung the top of it open so that he was half hidden behind it. 'You're about to receive gifts that will change your life,' he declared from behind the suitcase.

Mum and I exchanged a grin.

'That's quite a big expectation you're setting up there,' Mum said, laughing. 'I hope you mean in a good way?'

Tyler's head popped up over the suitcase. 'Of course!' he said, looking shocked, his hair springing up as if it was surprised too. 'I only use my genius for good. It's like the Force in *Star Wars* – I choose to use my powers for the right side.'

'Excellent stuff,' I said. 'But get on with it, will you?'

Tyler sniffed, pretending to be insulted but then couldn't help cracking a smile as he took out the first of his presents.

'Now this,' he said, 'is the first in the line of organisation assistance I've created.' He pulled out a canvas strip that was covered with pockets and clips. 'The Belt of All Things, I call it,' he said, handing it to Mum.

Mum took it and examined it. 'Oh, I see, this is where my phone can go . . . and here's where I can clip on my keys . . . and a place for pens . . .' She looked up. 'Tyler, this is great!'

Tyler smiled. 'Glad you like it.'

He delved back into the suitcase.

'For you,' he told me, handing over a package.

'I decided you need a new hobby.'

I nearly dropped it. 'It's really heavy!'

Tyler nodded. 'Yup, true genius doesn't come lightly.'

I tore the package open and started laughing.

'I'm tired of always being ahead of you,' Tyler explained as I pulled out what he'd given me. 'I mean, obviously I'm cleverer, but I don't have to be faster as well.'

I showed Mum what I was holding. 'Skater-Flyer Shoes,' I explained. I looked down at them, a bit overwhelmed. Tyler had decorated them with turquoise stripes and a bolt of lightning. 'Whoa! These are amazing. Thanks, Tyler.' I kept staring at them. I couldn't believe he'd gone to so much trouble.

'True,' Tyler said. 'But they're not *quite* as fast as mine, so don't be thinking you're going to win any races.'

'Hang on,' Mum said. 'Before you two go out roller-skate-flying or whatever it is those shoes do, can you please get out whatever else is in there – I'm dying of curiosity!'

Tyler bowed. 'With pleasure.'

I had to admit, Tyler had outdone himself. He'd made a magnetic board with a miniature window box attached to the bottom. Inside the window box were magnets with clips so you could attach them to things you wanted to stick up on the board. He called it the MagnaBoard (actually he called it the *Magnificent* MagnaBoard but even Mum rolled her eyes at that).

Then there was the Pocket Scarf – which was what it sounded like: a scarf covered in little pockets with flaps and buttons to keep stuff in. 'I didn't know you knew how to sew,' I said.

Tyler snorted. 'Are you kidding? Every self-respecting inventor knows how to sew. How do you think we invent more practical clothes?'

Mum's favourite was the Light Saver, where you attached individual fairy lights to objects you lost regularly – Tyler had made them sound-reactive, so when you clapped or whistled, the lights would come on. 'I can put one on my glasses,' Mum said, delighted. 'I'm always waking up in the night and can never find them in the dark. This is brilliant!'

'You know you'll be clapping and whistling all the time, right?' I told her.

'I'm a great whistler,' Mum reassured me, demonstrating. Which wasn't really my point.

Mum was thrilled. She went on so much about what a genius Tyler was that even he got a bit embarrassed in the end.

After tea, Mum said we could go to the park to try out my new Skater-Flyer Shoes while she cleaned up.

'Ready?' Tyler asked.

'Ready,' I told him.

Almost Flying

We ran down to the local park, which has a running track, and stopped at a bench to put our Skater-Flyer Shoes on. I'd thought they might be uncomfortable because of all the bits Tyler had built into them, but they were the most comfortable shoes I'd ever worn.

Tyler nodded when I mentioned it. 'I bend them round a bit so they're kind of worn in. When you go skater-flying, you don't want to be thinking that you're about to get a big blister on the back of your ankle. You want to be thinking about good stuff, like how fast you're going, and how you're about to beat your friend going around the track.' A breeze lifted up his hair so that it went in all directions. He grinned at me.

'What makes you so sure you're going to beat me? I've got your special invention on my feet now.'

'But you haven't got any skater-flyer hours, have

you? I have experience, my friend.'

I narrowed my eyes at him and waggled my eyebrows. 'We'll see.'

Tyler laughed. 'Mr Tull's right – you make some great faces.'

He showed me how to operate the remote for the shoes – one button to make the wings pop out, one to make the wheels pop out, and one for extra power.

'You sure you don't want a practice run first?' Tyler asked once I'd got the remote in my hand.

I shook my head. 'Let's go.'

Tyler nodded, his eyes gleaming. 'Once around the track?'

I crouched down low. 'OK. Ready, steady . . . go!'

We both took off. Tyler zigzagged expertly from side to side. I pressed the button for the wings and immediately felt my Skater-Flyer Shoes tipping to one side. Tyler was right – you probably did need some experience to use these shoes.

I leaned forward, pushing my feet out as fast as I could, slicing through the wind.

I heard Tyler laughing up ahead. 'Isn't it totally brilliant?' he shouted over his shoulder.

I crouched down even more so that I could swoop along in longer strides. 'Yes!' I shouted back. 'It's epic!'

The little wings at the side made a whirring sound and lifted the shoes up off the ground. It felt like I was about to soar into the sky. I was almost flying.

At the corner of the track, I pushed forward as hard as I could, catching a glimpse of a group of kids to the side, watching us open-mouthed. I wasn't invisible; I was standing out. I was doing everything you weren't supposed to do when you followed Sherlock code.

And it was great.

I think Tyler let me win – I'm pretty sure he slowed down as I sailed past him to cross the finish line. He was smiling as he caught up with me and did a spin on his wheels. 'Welcome to the world of skater-flyers,' he said.

'Thanks . . . that was amazing.'

It was more than amazing. It was the best day I'd had in years. I was finally discovering what it was like to have a real friend.

Numbers

I try not to think about Dad too much. Things like him dressing up every Christmas as an elf because he thought it was funnier than getting a Father Christmas outfit. (It was.) Or the way he used to take me to the fish-and-chip shop after we went swimming because he said that's when they tasted best. (They did.) Or the way he would stay outside practising football with me even when he was tired and it was cold and muddy. Or how he'd let me show him my Minecraft worlds even though I knew he didn't understand what I was doing.

Then there is the stuff I try *really* hard not to remember – the stuff from towards the end. How sometimes he was in the house but it was if he wasn't there because he didn't seem to hear anything we said. How he was always making excuses to go out as soon as Mum came in the door. How I wasn't able to make him smile any more.

Then how finally Mum sat me down and explained he was going away, trying to sound calm and in control, just like her Trouble Ninja self. How I listened to her level voice while her hands held mine. How she didn't seem to notice she was gripping my fingers really tightly, or that she was crying.

Dad left seven hundred and thirty days ago. I last saw him three hundred and ninety-three days ago. I don't know when I'll stop counting.

A Postcard

I should have been expecting it, but what with hanging out with Tyler, and being busy at home with Mum, I'd almost forgotten that it had been a couple of months since I'd had any post. But later that night, I found it on my bed, where Mum always put them.

A postcard – from Dad.

It didn't say much – but then they never did. A few lines about his job, the weather where he was and asking me how I liked the new house. And then the same PS and the same three words that he always put.

I turned it over. There was a photo of a tall tower and Dad had added an arrow pointing to the right of it. 'My place!'

I wondered what his flat was like and whether it felt empty when he came home after work. I wondered if he ever missed the mess that used to wind him up. I wondered if he still did funny voices and whether he knew what had happened to the stripy scarf he used to wear. I wondered if he actually missed me or whether the postcards were something he thought he had to write because he was my dad, like grown-up homework.

Whatever the answers were, I still wasn't ready to reply.

Questions and Answers

Another part of Sherlock code is to ask people questions. I'd always done it to avoid too much focus on me, but now it was different. When I asked Tyler about himself, I wanted to know the answers.

'You get on really well with your sister, don't you?' I asked him on the way to school one morning. We'd started meeting at the bus stop and walking in together. (It was a bit of a challenge because Tyler was usually late. Mr Tull had said that he was hoping my influence would rub off on Tyler eventually, but I think we both knew it was unlikely.)

'Yeah, Abby's great,' Tyler said. 'She fights for us both. Like when Mum and Dad didn't want her to do go-karting because they said it was too dangerous. She put together a PowerPoint presentation with facts and figures about how safe it was as long as you obeyed the rules.' Tyler darted forward to pick up a discarded trike wheel left out by someone's bin.

'Really? She did a whole presentation?'

'Oh yeah, Mum and Dad are always going on about the importance of "rational argument". So that's what Abby used. It worked too. She got to try go-kart racing, and that meant I could go too, as soon as I was old enough. I owe her.' He smiled at me. 'Also, when I was about six, one day I took off my socks at bedtime – you know, when they were a bit *worn in*.' He pinched his nose with his fingers and I laughed. 'I balled them up together, threw it at Dad and got him right in the nose.'

Having met Tyler's dad, I could imagine his expression when he'd got a face full of smelly socks.

'Abby said it was a Stink Sock Bomb and that I was an inventor – she didn't think I was just throwing smelly socks around; she thought I had good ideas. That was what got me started,' Tyler said. 'And she gives good advice too. Like when SnarkyMark's fan club wanted to start selling my stuff online.'

'What?' I went a bit cold. 'You mean Isaac and Libby?'

'Yeah, they talked to me about it, but I said I wasn't interested,' Tyler said.

'They wanted me to talk to you about it too,' I said.

I suddenly wished I'd said something when Isaac

and Libby first asked me. I wished it even more when I saw Tyler's expression. His hand clenched tight around the handle of his bag. 'Well, you can tell them I'm not interested in selling my ideas, thanks.'

'Sure, OK,' I said. 'I didn't think you would. That's kind of why I didn't mention it.' This was true, but it had been something else too – it was because I was worried what Tyler would think. That maybe he wouldn't like me any more.

Tyler glanced up at me and made a face. 'Sorry. It's just, those guys – they're only ever interested in making money, you know? They don't get what I do *at all*. They asked me about it ages ago and I said no. And now they're trying to get you to do their dirty work.'

I decided not to tell him how they'd wanted to surprise him and felt a lift of relief that I hadn't gone ahead and borrowed something like they'd asked.

'I'm glad you decided not to hang out with them so much,' Tyler said. 'I mean, not just because we got to be friends, but because they're not like you, are they?'

'I suppose not,' I said.

'But of course you worked out what they were like,' Tyler went on. 'When you move around a lot I guess you have to be good at figuring people out. That's why you're a good listener.'

I wasn't at all sure I was the person Tyler thought I was. If I had been, wouldn't I have talked to him before, once I'd worked out what Isaac and Libby were really like?

But I didn't say anything. I kept to the one bit of the Sherlock code I was good at.

Keeping my mouth shut.

The Conversation

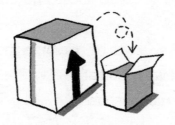

That afternoon I came home from school and wandered into the kitchen, making myself a drink and pulling out the biscuit tin. I'd called out when I came in, but hadn't heard any answer so I figured Mum had popped out.

I took my drink to the living-room area to see if there was any evidence that Tyler's inventions were working. That's when I heard a murmuring from upstairs and realised Mum must be on the phone. I ran upstairs to do my sign for 'Do you want a cup of tea?' when I heard her more clearly.

'I understand, Francis, I honestly do, but I'm not sure about making the commitment,' Mum was saying. I stopped outside her door instead of pushing it open as I would normally do. My skin felt clammy.

There was a pause. 'All right, I'll think it over, but I

can't make any promises.'

She started saying her goodbyes and I crept back down the stairs. I could hear her voice in my head – *I'm not sure about making the commitment.* They were almost the same words I'd heard her use once before when she turned down the offer of a new TV project. There was no question about it; Mum was planning on leaving her job. I'd thought she was enjoying it, but maybe she'd just been trying to make things here work for me.

I stared at the kettle as it boiled, my hand tight around the mug. If Mum left her job that would mean another move. We'd go and that would be it.

I'd made a big mistake by not following Sherlock code. I'd forgotten why I'd made it up in the first place, what it was protecting me from. I'd forgotten that the biggest danger was letting yourself care.

Night Thoughts

Over the weekend I couldn't sleep properly. I kept waking up in the middle of the night. The street lamp outside shone in through the window and I could see the outline of the postcard leaning on the shelf where I'd propped it. I wondered if Dad was awake too and if he'd know what to do.

I looked at the shadows of my Skater-Flyer Shoes sitting on my desk – my favourite possession apart from Geoffrey B. Stapleton. Tyler had put so much effort into them – so much effort into making friends with me. But what was the point if Mum and I would be moving on soon?

Learning not to think about things is like exercising a muscle, like the ones in your legs when you run. At first it's hard, and then your muscles get stronger and you find it easier and easier. That was what it had been like with Dad. I blocked everything out and practised not thinking about him, because that's what made it possible to get through every day without missing him too much, without feeling the way I did when he first left.

If we moved away I'd have two people to miss, two people to try and block out.

Mum always said things seem worse in the middle of the night, that it all looks more hopeful and more positive in the morning. I tried and tried to think of an answer that would mean she was right.

The Freeze-Out

By Monday morning, I knew what I had to do. If Mum and I were going to move, then the more I hung out with Tyler, the harder it would be when we left. The sooner we both got used to it the better. I had to go back to following Sherlock code – properly.

On the way to school I felt heavy, like I'd eaten too much, too quickly. I put the Skater-Flyer Shoes Tyler had given me in a bag and left early to avoid meeting him on the way. It wouldn't take long for him to get the message if I did things according to the code.

That's what I figured anyway. But it turned out Tyler wasn't an easy person to blank out.

'Hey! Where were you?' Tyler bounced up to me as we were settling into our places before registration. He didn't bother waiting for the answer though; he was too excited to get to what he wanted to tell me. 'Guess what?'

'Hey,' I said, busying myself with getting out my pencil case and acting like I hadn't heard his question. It didn't make any difference as Tyler just carried on anyway.

'I was talking to our new neighbour over the weekend and it turns she has pets. *Unusual pets.*'

Normally I would have been onto this straight away, but now I nodded without expression, as if he'd said, 'It turns out she quite enjoys chocolate biscuits.'

Tyler frowned slightly at my lack of response but I guess he thought I was just tired, or hadn't realised how interesting it was.

'She has a ferret, three parrots and a llama,' he went on. 'She takes them all out for walks – though not at the same time obviously.' He looked thoughtful for a minute. 'I wonder if that's because they'd fight. I should ask her. I wonder who'd win?'

'Uh-huh,' I said in as flat a tone as possible. 'That's funny.'

'Funny? It's brilliant!' Tyler said. 'Finally we have an interesting neighbour! And just think of all the things she must need for them.'

'What, like leads?' Zoe said, coming up to us.

'Yeah, exactly,' Tyler said. 'Special leads for ferrets, parrots and llamas, or a feeding station or whatever. I could invent a whole line of animal-related brilliance. Imagine what a help that would be! This could be how I make my name!' He looked over to me, waiting for me to say something, but I didn't. His smile dimmed a little, but then Zoe asked him if he could find out whether ferrets really went up people's trousers and he turned to answer her, which gave me the chance to slip away and offer to help Mr Tull give out the worksheets for the first lesson.

That wasn't the end of it though. All day Tyler kept trying to start conversations with me, and I kept giving him the smallest possible response. It wasn't easy to ignore him, especially when he said things like, 'Did you know that llamas take *five whole minutes to pee*?' but by the end of the afternoon he seemed to have got the idea. Just before last break, he came up close. 'What's going on, Jack?'

'Nothing,' I told him.

'Have I annoyed you or something?' He looked me full in the face.

I looked away, avoiding his eyes. 'Of course not.'

'So why aren't you talking to me?'

'I am.'

'You know what I mean,' Tyler said.

'No, I don't,' I said. Then I took the chance to do what I'd been trying to summon up the nerve to do all day. My stomach clenched as I dug into my backpack to pull out the smaller bag I'd brought in. 'But listen – I think you'd better have these back. I don't think they're right for me.'

Tyler looked inside the bag and then back up at me. 'You don't think Skater-Flyer Shoes are *right* for you?'

'No.' Keep it simple, keep it safe, I told myself.

Tyler put them back on my desk. 'I don't want them back,' he said, his voice flat. 'They're not even my size.'

I shrugged and headed out the door. I didn't look behind me. I guess Tyler took the bag after all because when I came back it was gone. Not only that, but after break he didn't bother trying to talk to me any more. Which should have been a relief, but just made me wish I was already on my way to School Seven.

The Discovery

Two days before Dad left, I came home from school by myself for the first time. Mum had given me a key after she and Dad had agreed that I was old enough to walk home from school on my own. We only lived a few doors away so I didn't even have to cross a road. The teachers had said that it was fine and I'd been really pleased. It felt like a big deal, as if somehow I was a bit more grown-up.

I guess Dad had forgotten about it, or maybe he wasn't expecting me back so early, but in any case he didn't hear the front door open. And he didn't hear me coming upstairs where he was talking on his mobile. At first, not paying attention, I barely heard what he was saying. But then I heard him loud and clear even though he was talking quietly.

'I wish it wasn't true, but it is. There's nothing left to stay for.'

Out of Practice

After school I came home to a note from Mum saying she had a meeting at work and would be home late. She'd left dinner in the fridge and instructions for when to put it in the oven. It was already more like the old days and we hadn't even moved yet.

I went upstairs and lay on my bed, looking at the ceiling. I used to do that in our first house, after Dad left. I'd practised blotting things out so that I wasn't thinking or feeling anything at all. By the time we moved I was already pretty good at it, and by the third move, I'd nailed it. I tried it now. But Tyler's grin when he was showing me a new invention kept flashing into my mind. Every time I tried to bat the image away I'd hear his voice saying, 'You will *not* believe this bit of epicness!' Then I'd think of how well his Skater-Flyer Shoes had fitted me. And how when I'd said so, Tyler had replied, 'Yeah, it's almost as if someone made them especially for you, isn't it?' and we'd cracked up laughing. Every time I'd shut up one memory, another would pop up in its place like a jack-in-a-box. Which was what I felt like – Jack in a box, with no way out. So I kept on staring up at the ceiling, hoping I'd figure out how to follow Sherlock code again.

At our old house the cluster of cracks in the ceiling had looked like a spider's web. I'd spent ages trying count how many there were. In the end it hadn't mattered, because the real cracks turned out not to be in the ceiling at all.

Changes

Because Tyler had become the main person I hung out with, now we weren't speaking I ended up alone at school. Isaac and Libby seemed to have lost any interest in me helping them with Project Moneybags. They stopped asking me if I'd managed to borrow anything from Tyler and spent all their time having long whispered conversations together. They were probably only talking about SnarkyMark, but it still reminded me of how lucky they were to have someone they could hang out with. I didn't have anyone. Meanwhile, Tyler had slotted back into his usual role of being friendly with everyone, and I was left on the sidelines. No one was nasty, but no one went out of their way to be particularly nice either. I got the impression from Zoe that she thought I'd been mean to Tyler and wasn't too impressed. To be fair, I couldn't blame her.

Mum started to be out more, so that was different too. I'd tried to ask her about work a couple of times, but she'd said everything was fine. By the end of the week I was desperate to know when we were going to be leaving. I'd forgotten something else about following Sherlock code. It was boring. With Tyler there had *always* been something to think about. Now I was back to being just Jack – the person with no personality. And that was the problem. Seeing Tyler every day reminded me how good it had felt to be a real person, not a pretend character.

I wouldn't make the same mistake again.

Awkward Questions

Two days after I'd blanked out Tyler, Mr Tull asked me to stay behind at break to help him tidy up a science experiment (some of the class had got a bit 'enthusiastic' with the vinegar and sodium bicarbonate). I was glad he asked me, because break times aren't exactly fun when you don't have anyone to talk to. It's what I'd been aiming for, but it still felt weird. It was such a contrast to just a few days ago when Tyler and I would talk non-stop or joke around with some of the others.

I was wiping down the tables when Mr Tull spoke. 'Jack, have you and Tyler fallen out about something?'

I hesitated. Mr Tull wasn't stupid and he was the kind of teacher who cared about his class getting on, so if I said a straight no and he didn't believe me (and I didn't think he would), he would keep on asking questions. I decided telling a bit of the truth was the best way forward. 'I just think it's best if we don't hang out together so much,' I said.

'Did he upset you? Say something out of turn?' Mr Tull straightened up from where he'd been sweeping up the spilled bicarb with a dustpan and brush.

'No! It's nothing to do with him, honestly,' I said. The last thing I wanted was to get Tyler into trouble.

'Good,' Mr Tull said, looking relieved. 'I know Tyler can be quite . . . exuberant, but I've never known him to be intentionally unkind.'

'We didn't fight or anything,' I said.

'But you think it's best that you don't spend time with each other?' Mr Tull's voice was gentle but he sounded confused.

I was about to make up some excuse and then I decided not to. I told him the real reason. 'My mum's going to leave her job, so we'll be moving soon,' I said. 'We move a lot. It's better, easier, if I don't get too friendly with people.'

Mr Tull frowned. 'But even if her job changes, why would that mean you have to move?'

I stared at the cloth in my hand. For the last two years, whenever Mum had got a new job, it *always* meant a move. It hadn't occurred to me that if she left this job she might just get a different job in the same town. Would she really do that? Then I thought of how light she always seemed when we left a place and made a fresh start somewhere new – like she thought this time everything would work out, this time everything would be different. She had tried to make it work here and it hadn't. That meant we'd be going soon. I didn't know how else to explain it though. 'It's what's always happens.'

Mr Tull didn't say anything for a minute. He put the dustpan and brush away. 'I think maybe you need to talk to your mum, Jack,' he said. 'And I think maybe you need to talk to Tyler too. It strikes me that you've been coping with things for a long time and that you might not realise that situations can change. That even people can change.'

I nodded like I understood and we finished clearing up. Teachers know a lot of things, but that didn't mean Mr Tull was right.

A Shock

Mum was home when I got back from school. As soon as I walked in she looked up from the sofa where she was stretched out, reading from a thick wad of papers that was balanced on her lap.

'Hey, sweetheart – come and have a chat.'

This was it, I thought. She was going to tell me about leaving her job. Maybe she was even going to say where we were going next.

As I wandered over, Mum smiled. 'Have you noticed what's different about me recently?'

I thought maybe she was trying to lead me gently into the subject. Was I supposed to say I'd noticed that she wasn't happy? Except that if I thought about it, she hadn't seemed particularly unhappy apart from that one phone call. And if she was about to tell me bad news, why was she smiling?

'Um, no, not really,' I said.

'I haven't lost my glasses or my phone once since Tyler gave me my essentials belt,' Mum said proudly. 'And haven't you noticed how much tidier I've become since he gave me the MagnaBoard?'

'Oh, sure, yeah.' Actually I *hadn't* noticed. Probably because I'd been too busy thinking about when we were going to move to realise she hadn't been asking me to look for things all the time.

'You'll have to ask Tyler round again so that I can thank him,' Mum told me. 'How is he anyway?'

I shrugged. 'Fine.'

Mum frowned slightly. 'Everything all right between you two?'

'Sure,' I said. I wasn't up to filling her in.

Mum took a sip of tea. 'I'm so happy that you've found a good friend here. That's what I was hoping would happen. It means we're finally putting down roots.'

I stared at her. This didn't sound like the start of the 'It's not working out here' conversation at all.

Mum went on, not seeming to notice my confused expression. 'Actually I have something quite exciting to tell you,' she said.

Was this it? What was going on?

'What?'

'Francis is promoting me – from administrator to manager,' Mum said, breaking into a smile.

'What?' I felt my mouth go slack – Mum *wasn't* leaving her job?

'He asked me a couple of weeks ago. I didn't say yes right away because it means committing to staying, and you know for the last few years we haven't exactly been settled anywhere. I had to be sure it was the right decision.' Mum smiled. 'But you've seemed so happy here, and I have to admit I've never enjoyed a job as much as this one. There aren't any celebrity tantrums or impossible deadlines or endless stress about budgets. And more than anything else, it feels as if what I'm doing actually matters.'

I stared at the floor. None of what Mum had said was what I'd been expecting.

'Jack? Are you OK?' Mum sounded worried.

'I heard you talking on the phone the other week,' I said, still not looking up. 'And you said you didn't know if you could make the commitment. I thought you meant work.'

I looked up and saw Mum looking puzzled. 'I don't . . .'

Then her forehead cleared. '*Oh*. Yes, I was talking to Francis about taking on more responsibility. It felt like such a big commitment – well, it is. But I think it's a good one.'

'You don't want to leave your job and move somewhere else?'

'No, of course not.' Mum said, her eyebrows raised. 'Is that what you thought?'

I nodded, feeling my cheeks heat up.

'Oh, Jack,' Mum said. 'Why didn't you just ask me?'

I shrugged, not wanting to say why, not really even knowing why I hadn't, except I'd been so afraid that I was right.

But being wrong didn't feel as good as it should have. Because I'd already messed everything up.

From Bad to Worse

It was another night without much sleep. Knowing that Mum had actually been deciding to stay for longer, not leave, had thrown all my usual survival plans in the air. There was a moment when I almost wished that we *were* moving again, because I felt so embarrassed and bad about the way I'd frozen Tyler out. And it was weird to think of not moving, of giving up Sherlock code for good. It made me half excited and half terrified. But then I realised the most important thing. Staying meant I could go back to being Tyler's friend.

If he'd let me.

The next day at school I tried to catch Tyler's eye before registration, but he turned his back on me as I said hello. I was a bit surprised. We hadn't been talking much (except for 'Can you pass the pencil sharpener' and stuff like that in lessons), but we had been politely nodding to each other every now and again. The way Tyler turned his back so deliberately seemed different. It looked as if getting him to accept my apology was going to be even harder than I'd been afraid it would be.

At break, Tyler sped out of the door as if the fire alarm had gone off and he could smell smoke. As I started to go after him, Mr Tull stopped me.

'Jack? Have you talked to Tyler yet?'

I shook my head, not looking him in the eye. I didn't know what to say – Mr Tull had told me what to do and I'd ignored him. I thought he was going to give me another mini-lecture, but he looked worried. 'I think something's bothering him,' he said. 'He seems upset. If he mentions anything to you, or if you hear anything from someone else, can you let me know?'

'I'll try, but I don't think he's my biggest fan right now.'

Mr Tull smiled. 'I realise you aren't such good friends at the moment, but often things have a way of working out. And maybe, Jack, you could *both* use a friend right now.'

Once we were back in the classroom for the next lesson, I looked at Tyler and saw that Mr Tull was right; there *was* something wrong with him. He had big dark circles under his eyes as if he'd got even less sleep than I had. He looked as if he'd shrunk into himself somehow – like there was something going on inside his head the whole time that wasn't letting him think about anything else. I knew that look. I knew that feeling. And I hated thinking of Tyler feeling that way too.

After school, I walked up to Tyler quickly as he was getting his coat from the hook in the corridor. It felt like taking off a plaster – better to do it in one rip.

'Hi,' I said.

Tyler looked shocked, and then his mouth set into a thin line. 'Hello,' he said.

It was going to be even harder than I'd imagined. 'Look, I want to say sorry.'

'For . . . ?' Tyler raised his eyebrows as if he had no idea what I was talking about. Clearly he wasn't going to make this easy. Not that I could blame him.

'For blanking you. Ignoring you,' I said.

Oh, that,' Tyler shrugged, as if he'd hardly noticed. His expression still said, 'And I care because . . . ?'

'I thought Mum was leaving her job,' I said. 'So I thought we'd be moving.'

Tyler kept staring at me. 'And . . . ?'

'And I thought it would be easier . . . if we stopped

hanging out together. Then maybe it wouldn't be so hard when we weren't able to be mates after I'd left.' I trailed off. Said out loud, my Sherlock code didn't sound as clever as I'd always thought it was.

'So you thought you'd trash your friendships before you left? Is that why you gave your Skater-Flyer Shoes to Isaac and Libby?' Tyler looked me in the eye, his voice cold.

I'd been expecting Tyler to have a go at me for dropping him, but I hadn't been expecting this. 'What?'

'I'm getting it now,' he went on, picking up speed. 'Basically, instead of making the most of the time you had to hang out with me, and maybe work out how to keep in touch and organise visits after you'd moved away, you decided it was better to make sure the friendship didn't exist any more. So you betrayed me.' Tyler shook his head. 'Interesting approach.'

My skin felt clammy. 'I don't know what you're talking about,' I said. 'I didn't give Libby and Isaac anything. I tried to give the shoes back to *you*.'

'You already told me they asked you to help them, Jack. It's a bit late to be denying it.' He looked away, as if the sight of me made him feel sick.

'But I *didn't*!' I felt myself flushing. I knew I hadn't given Libby and Isaac anything, but the fact that they'd asked me made me feel guilty anyway. And it sounded as if what had happened was still my fault even if it hadn't been on purpose. If I hadn't tried to give the Skater-Flyer Shoes back, they'd never have got hold of them.

'Their website's called *Skate n Fly*,' Tyler said. 'The Skater-Flyer Shoes are right there on the first page. I don't see how you can deny they're the ones I made you. I'd call that evidence, wouldn't you? Know what else? They're advertising other pairs, which means they're copying my idea. Which they can because – thanks to you – they've got my design.'

'Honestly, Tyler, I didn't know anything about it,' I said. 'I mean, I knew they were planning a website but –'

'But you didn't know what they were planning to sell?' Tyler looked at me, incredulous.

'Yes. I mean, I knew they *wanted* to sell your stuff, but I wasn't going to help them.'

Tyler looked at me. 'Why should I believe you? You go around pretending to be different people to make sure everyone likes you. You drop friends as soon as you think you're going to be moving on.' He pointed at me. 'You do whatever it takes to make sure you're all right, without caring about anyone else.'

He walked away before I could answer. Not that I had any idea what to say.

Skate n Fly

The website looked professional – Isaac and Libby's brother was obviously good at the whole 'marketing' thing. The Skater-Flyer Shoes Tyler had made me were right on the home page, just like Tyler had said. A big close-up of them. Underneath them was the caption: *Time to skate n fly! – Let us know you're interested by filling in the form and we'll email you when our fantastic creation is in production!* Isaac and Libby weren't even selling Tyler's invention on his behalf like they said they would – they were stealing it.

I thought about going downstairs and telling Mum I didn't want to live here after all, that I wanted to move on. I saw how easy that would be – another chance for a fresh start with no responsibilities, no guilt.

A little voice in my head added, *Another chance to run away.*

The next morning, I went straight up to Isaac and Libby.

'You stole Tyler's shoes,' I said.

Isaac spread out his hands. 'Hey, we didn't steal anything. We just found something that no one wanted and took it.'

'What do you mean, no one wanted it?'

Libby smiled, like she'd been looking forward to the question. 'We *heard* you, Jack – you told Ty you didn't want the shoes any more, and he told you he didn't want them back. We figured that since neither of you wanted them, we'd give them a good home, right?'

'On a website,' I said.

Isaac laughed. 'You've got to get on it to make it.'

'You can't steal his idea,' I said. 'It's illegal.'

'The thing is, it's a bit more complicated than that, Jack,' Isaac said. 'See, our brother's been learning about patents. It's like this special . . . thing . . . that means if you haven't got one on your idea, someone else can use it. And Tyler doesn't have one.'

'We're not being harsh,' Libby said. 'We're just being practical.'

'Exactly,' Isaac said. 'We're not going to be nasty about it or anything. I'm sure our brother will give Ty a bit of a thank-you later.'

'He's doing Skate n Fly as part of his college project,' Libby said.

'He'll get a really good mark,' Isaac said. 'And we'll make loads of money.'

They high-fived each other.

'You need to take the website down and give the shoes back,' I said.

Isaac shrugged. 'It's not going to happen, yeah?'

'Well, something's going to happen,' I told them. It was the best I could come up with at short notice and it wasn't good enough, because they both laughed. I clenched my fists in my pockets and glared at them. I guess Tyler and Mr Tull were right about my ability to make faces, because when they saw my expression, they stopped laughing.

'Hey, Jack, it's not a big deal,' Libby said. 'Tyler's always making stuff. He can just make something else.'

'It *is* a big deal,' I said. 'And he's not going to have to make something else because you're going to give the shoes back.' I swivelled round and walked away. The one thing I knew was that I was done with going along with what Isaac and Libby wanted.

I found Tyler in a corner of the football pitch reading from a heavy-looking book. He was frowning and rubbing his eyes. He looked exhausted.

'Tyler,' I said.

He looked up and sighed. 'Not got the message yet, Jack? I'm not interested.'

'Look,' I said. 'I'm sorry. I didn't give the Skater-Flyer Shoes to them, but I know it's my fault they got hold of them. And I'm sorry about the way I handled thinking we were moving – you know, ignoring you and everything. It's just – that was how I used to deal with things.'

Tyler shrugged. 'Yeah. You either take the risk when you make a friend, or you don't. I do and you don't. So we're not the same anyway. You were right.'

'No,' I said. 'I wasn't.'

Tyler sighed, putting his finger to mark his place in the book. 'The thing is, Jack, I don't really care any more. I've got bigger problems now.'

'The patent?'

Tyler's head jerked up. 'How did you know?'

'I tried to get the shoes back from them.'

'*That's* not going to happen.' He held up the book. 'But I'll tell you what is going to happen. Isaac's brother is going to register my idea and make loads of money with it.'

'Can your mum or dad help?'

Tyler shrugged. 'Lawyers cost money and we don't

have a lot, so I'm not going to ask them. They worry enough as it is.' He threw the book down. 'It's pointless me trying to read up on it. There's nothing I can do.'

It was weird seeing Tyler feeling hopeless and giving up. It felt like the sort of thing I would do, not him.

'I want to help,' I told him.

'You can't,' Tyler said. 'And to be honest, I'm not sure why you'd expect me to trust you anyway.'

Tyler was right – he didn't have any reason to trust me. But whether he did or didn't, I knew there was something I could do. I just didn't know if I could face it.

Just Three Words

Every postcard Dad sends has a PS on it with the same three words.

Please call me.

I'd stopped calling him soon after he started his new job. It was always so awkward, so hard. I never knew what to say. Everything that came out of my mouth sounded flat and boring. And deep down I knew he probably didn't *really* want to talk to me. That he was just waiting to get off the phone and go back to his new life. A life without complications and annoyances. A life without me and Mum.

But then I thought of Tyler. I thought of how all the things he made were designed to help other people. I thought of how everything I'd done was designed to protect myself.

It was about time I became a bit more like Tyler.

The Telling

I couldn't call Dad to ask for his help without telling Mum. That was hard because I thought she'd be upset. I might have guessed by now – I was wrong again.

'I'm so pleased you're getting in touch with him,' she said. 'I didn't want to push you but I've been hoping you'd change your mind.'

'You have?' I thought I'd understood everything, and it was becoming more and more obvious I hadn't understood anything at all.

'It's time to forgive him, Jack,' Mum said. 'It's time to move on.' She smiled at me. 'Especially now that we're *not* moving house any time soon.'

She was right – so I told her everything.

When I'd finished her eyes were shiny. 'Oh, Jack, he didn't mean – Did you really think it was your fault that your dad and I broke up?'

'Not completely,' I said. 'I mean, I just thought maybe I'd got difficult to look after. That I could have behaved better or, I don't know, been more fun to be around, not so annoying. Then maybe he would have stayed for longer . . .' I trailed off. She was shaking her head.

'You were the reason he stayed *so long,*' Mum said. She put her hand under my chin and tipped it up so that she could look me in the eyes. 'Your dad and I got together very young. We kept growing and changing because that's what people do – even when they're not kids any more – and once we'd changed we weren't right for each other any more. Sometimes people don't grow in the same direction.'

She was looking at me hard, as if she was trying to read my mind. She took her hand away from my face and reached for my hand, threading her fingers through mine. 'Listen. I don't regret a single second with your dad, but I know that we're both happier apart than we could be together. But not one thing about us breaking up was your fault, Jack. *Not one thing.* There was nothing you could have said or done to make the situation turn out differently – do you understand? You didn't do anything wrong. He loves you every bit as much as I do.'

Hearing that made me feel a bit like I had when Tyler

and I went out on his Skater-Flyer Shoes and we'd gone really fast. A bit dizzy and out of control – as if I might actually take off and fly. I'd thought that maybe if I'd been a different person, a different, better version of myself, that Mum and Dad would still be together. But I'd been wrong about that as well.

Mum squeezed my hand. 'I've made a lot of mistakes, Jack. I thought it was better not to talk about Dad too much. I thought it was OK that we were on the move all the time.' She shook her head. 'I guess I had this image of us being adventurous and carefree – not getting too involved with anyone or anywhere, but that's not how it works, is it? You have to be part of something. You have to commit to places and the people in them.' She leaned towards me so her forehead was touching mine and then pulled away and smiled. 'Maybe we can start putting things right. What do you think?'

'Sounds good,' I told her.

So it turned out that we'd both been doing the same thing, thinking that keeping ourselves safe from other people was the best way to be.

That night Mum and I made a lot of plans and one big decision. It was time for us to be part of something.

I Prove I'm Not an Inventor

Tyler might not want to hear what I had to say, but I was going to make him listen in the best way I knew how. Or the best way *he* knew how. I invented something.

At school the next day, I came in early. This time I wasn't trying to talk to Tyler; I was trying to surprise him. I snuck into the classroom and went over to our table and put my creation down on his side. Then I sank down into my usual place and waited.

When Tyler came in, I looked over and saw his eyebrows go up as he noticed the package. He didn't say anything but glanced over at me, keeping his expression neutral. I sat and waited.

Tyler pulled out his chair and sat down, dropping his bag on the table between us so that my view of the package was blocked. I might not have been able to see what he was doing but I could hear him. The newspaper I'd wrapped my invention in crackled as it came off.

I waited – and then I heard a snort. I tried to keep my smile from breaking out but couldn't help giggling when I heard the whirr of the wind-up mechanism and the clash of cymbals.

'What is this supposed to be exactly?'

I turned to face Tyler. He wasn't actually smiling but he looked a lot more friendly.

'I thought it would be obvious,' I said. 'It's an apology monkey.'

Tyler looked down at my ancient clockwork toy monkey (you wind him up and he bashes cymbals together). I'd put a little sign between the monkey's hands that unfolded when his arms were pushed apart to reveal the words 'Sorry, sorry, sorry'.

There was a long silence as Tyler looked from the monkey happily bashing his cymbals to me. Then he broke into a wide smile. 'From now on, I think we can agree that you leave the inventing up to me.'

I grinned back. 'It's a deal.'

The next great moment was at break when I told Tyler what my dad did for a living and what he was going to do.

'You're kidding me?' he said.

Actually he said it several times.

Eventually he shook his whole body, like a dog shaking off water, and leapt to his feet. 'You know, you should have told me being friends with you again would be *useful*. I would have stopped being angry ages ago.'

Then he punched me in the arm and we started laughing so hard that Mr Tull came over to see what all the noise was about. I don't think he was bothered though, because once he'd realised we weren't fighting, I caught his eye and he winked and nodded at me, as if I'd finally done what he'd been hoping I would.

The Showdown

'I don't know how they could not feel bad about claiming they'd come up with the shoes,' Tyler said as we prepared our plans. 'I mean, they were basically pretending to be me.'

'I kind of pretended to be other people in all my other schools,' I said, wondering if that made me no better than Isaac and Libby.

'Yeah, but you weren't trying to make yourself look good,' Tyler said. 'Or ripping off other people's ideas to make money.' His eyes glinted. 'Or if you were, you were rubbish at it . . .'

I laughed. It felt good to be back to teasing each other again.

'So are you ready to face them?' I said.

'I can't wait.'

I'd told the twins that Tyler wanted to meet them after school to talk about future plans. They took it to mean that Tyler had accepted what they'd done and thought he might as well go along with it, which is what we'd been hoping they would think.

They were both looking pleased with themselves as we walked up to them.

'I'm glad you're coming on board, Ty,' Isaac said. 'And look, let's get the awkward bit out the way, yeah? I know our brother is getting the legal bit done on the shoes, but if you want to give us something else to sell, we can sort out a deal, right? We want you to do well. You're our favourite supplier.'

Tyler snorted. 'I'm your *only* supplier,' he said. 'And not on purpose. But anyway, we don't have something give you; we've got something to *tell* you.'

Isaac and Libby exchanged a look, their smiles falling slightly.

'It's about Jack.'

Now they just looked confused.

I glanced at Tyler and saw he was chewing his lip to stop himself from laughing.

'Oh?' Isaac looked like a snake that had gone to eat a mouse and then discovered that the mouse had fangs.

'Yeah,' I said, 'I've got some good news. You see, my

dad's a lawyer. And he happens to be a patent lawyer. Isn't that *hilarious*?'

'Hilarious,' Isaac repeated after me in a whisper.

Libby looked like she'd swallowed slime by accident.

'And he's sorting out patents for Tyler's designs. All of them.' I smiled and waggled my eyebrows at them. 'He works fast too.'

'Yeah, first up were my shoes. You know the ones, Isaac,' Tyler said. 'The Skater-Flyer Shoes you and Libby stole from the classroom and uploaded onto a website. Without asking me.'

'It's interesting actually,' I added. 'Because it turns out there *are* laws to stop people from doing that. And you and your brother have broken them.'

It got quite heated after that, but it ended up with three things being very clear:

Tyler and I were friends again.

Isaac, Libby and their brother would not be getting any further (or richer) with Project Moneybags.

Dad was still someone I could count on.

All the Grown-Ups Pile In

Once I'd spoken to Dad, Mum called Tyler's parents. And then Tyler's mum called Mr Tull, and Mr Tull called Isaac and Libby's parents, and then basically a lot of grown-ups got very loud and the following things happened:

We got the Skater-Flyer Shoes Tyler had made me back.

Isaac and Libby's brother had to take the Skate n Fly website down and had to do his college project about the advertising plans of the local garage.

Isaac and Libby were banned from watching SnarkyMark for three months (even Tyler and I thought that was harsh).

And Tyler and I got really, really good at racing in Skater-Flyer Shoes.

Mr Tull Lightens the Atmosphere

It wasn't that we weren't friendly with Isaac and Libby; it was more that it was all a bit awkward. Every time Tyler or I looked in their direction, they looked down at the floor as if they wished they could disappear. They didn't chat much either, even to each other. I *almost* missed hearing them talking about SnarkyMark.

'I think we need to draw a line under all of this,' Mr Tull told us one day after he'd asked Tyler and me to stay behind at break. 'I know what they did was very serious, but I do think they feel bad about it.'

We nodded. Even though we'd been angry, we were both happy to move on. 'I'm ready to let it go,' Tyler said. 'I'm having too much fun with Jack these days to be bothered about it any more. And we got the shoes back anyway.'

'Good,' Mr Tull looked relieved. 'Because I don't think I can keep teaching a class where two people look that miserable.'

'Yeah. I do feel a bit sorry for them,' Tyler said. 'They can't even watch SnarkyMark to cheer themselves up. I mean, if someone told me I couldn't invent things for three months, I'd probably spontaneously combust.'

'I'd spontaneously combust if I *had* to watch it,' I told him. 'But I know what you mean.'

'That's great to hear,' Mr Tull said. 'Because I've come up with an idea to replace SnarkyMark in Isaac and Libby's affections. And maybe teach them something about respecting creativity too.'

Mr Tull's idea was epic. He gathered up the school's tablets and set up an after-school club where he got us all making stop-motion movies using a couple of apps and a *lot* of Lego.

Isaac and Libby *loved* it and stopped talking about anything else. They created a character called MarkyMark ('I wonder where they got their inspiration,' Tyler said) and they talked about him as much as they used to go on about SnarkyMark. After Mr Tull had put the four of us together one afternoon to start work on a new film, Tyler showed the twins a Lego transformer he'd created (it turned from a spaceship into a four-headed alien).

'See, that's what everyone should be doing,' Isaac said. 'Making stuff, *real* stuff. Not chasing after money. Money just brings you trouble. It's *evil*.'

'No more Project Moneybags then?' I smiled.

Isaac flushed. 'That was when I was a bit young, yeah? The thing you want to be is a creator. Like Ty.'

I knew what Isaac meant. I wanted to be like Tyler too. But I was starting to think that being like myself was OK too.

Mum had taken some of Tyler's inventions into the care home, where they were a huge hit – it turned out that everyone needed a MagnaBoard when they got older. Tyler loved knowing his inventions were helping people, and Dad had registered all his patents so now Tyler's mum was talking about getting a couple of them made.

'See? You're a real inventor now,' I told him.

Tyler raised his eyebrows in mock outrage. 'What do you mean, "real"? I always was!' But I could tell he was pleased.

*

It was still a while before I got out of the habit of following Sherlock code completely. Tyler had to remind me that I didn't need to be so careful around people, or so reluctant to say what I thought. And it took time to get used to the idea of home being really home. Basically, I wasn't used to the idea of belonging.

Homecoming

When the day came, I was still nervous – but it was the good, excited kind, not the jittery, stomach-churning kind. I packed my bag and went down to wait.

When I heard the knock on the door, I glanced over at the postcard and the arrow pointing to 'My place!' that was now pinned to the board in the kitchen. They'd both said from now on I had two homes – and this weekend I was about to see the second one. I took a deep breath and opened the door.

He was wearing the blue-and-white stripy scarf and a huge smile. 'Hey, buddy.'

'Hey, Dad.'

For a second we stood grinning at each other. Then Dad put his arms around me to pull me close in a hug so tight that his coat scratched my face and the row of buttons dug into my shirt. Underneath the coat I could feel his heart thumping, hard and fast like mine. 'Do you have any idea how much I've missed you?' Dad whispered into my hair.

I tried to speak, but I couldn't. I tried to nod and then shook my head.

'I've missed you too,' I whispered into his chest.

Dad hugged me even harder. 'Right then. Let's make sure we can't miss each other for so long ever again. Deal?'

'Deal.'

At that moment, if I could have been anyone and anywhere in the world I wouldn't have swapped places. I was happy to be just Jack.

Acknowledgements

Olin Miller said, 'Writing is the hardest way of earning a living, with the possible exception of wrestling alligators'. I'd say that sometimes wrestling alligators seems the more attractive career path. Fliss Johnston must be thanked for not only coaxing the early idea for this book into something resembling a story but also for remaining patient, kind, wise and encouraging as I wrestled this particular alligator into shape. (I don't know where editors get their patience from, but I do know they seem to have it in vast supply.) Fliss gave her editorial expertise generously and extensively – if this story works, it's because of her. Enormous thanks to Talya Baker, the ever-vigilant copy editor who braves the Internet universe to research lightsaber colours and Star Wars etiquette to make sure I'm not made a fool of in front of a well-informed readership (and my kids). Alex Gunn did another fantastic job with both the cover and the illustrations – the last image in the book tugs my heart, every time – thank you. And of course thanks must also go to the rest of the supportive, enthusiastic and hard-working Piccadilly team: marketing manager Charlotte Hoare, PR manager Tina Mories, and proofreader Jane Hammett. Thanks too to my mother, my wider family, and my friends for being such a strong source of support – you know how I feel about you all (but I'm happy to repeat myself any time).

Most of all, I have to thank my husband, Neil, and my children, Evie and Noah, for cheering me on, putting up with me during the less attractive stages of writing a book (pretty much all of them) and for every single day being the best prize a writer could ever have.

About the Author

The first book in Kate Scott's comedy-adventure series for Piccadilly Press, *Spies in Disguise: Boy in Tights*, won a Lancashire Fantastic Book Award and books in the series are also published in Denmark and the USA. Kate's most recent novel, *Giant*, has been nominated, longlisted and shortlisted for a number of regional awards and was described by Frank Cottrell Boyce as 'Fresh and funny . . . a book that celebrates friendship and the power of being true to yourself.' Kate has written fiction and non-fiction for Oxford University Press, Pearson, HarperCollins and Hodder. She is also a published poet, a playwright, and a scriptwriter for children's television. Follow Kate on Twitter: @KateScottWriter

Have you read GIANT?

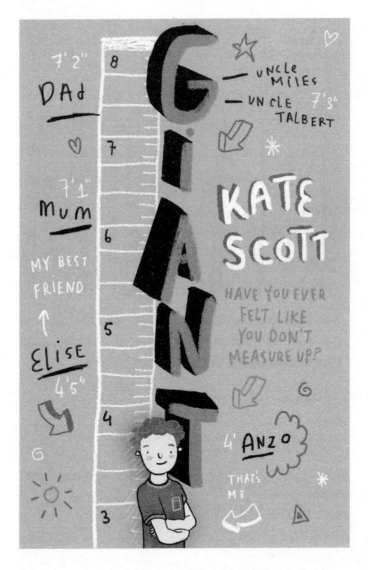

Turn the page for a sneak preview . . .

See this? You probably think that the person the size of a shrub is standing in a forest, next to the trunks of some very large trees.

Those trees are my family. That shrub next to them? That's me.

It Didn't Start Well

Mum and Dad probably didn't mean to land me in trouble as soon as I was born. To be fair, since they were unusually tall, and Dad's brothers were unusually tall, and their parents were unusually tall, naming me Anzo must have seemed like an obvious thing to do. In case you don't know, in ancient German, *Anzo* means 'giant'. Which is a problem when it turns out that you're definitely *not* a giant. And an even bigger problem if you're unusually short. Maybe if I'd been named something normal, like Tom, Josh Gurney wouldn't have thought of lifting me up and hanging me on a coat peg, saying, '*Now* you're a giant!'

But I'd never know because I was stuck with being Anzo − and a shrub.

* * *

The day I thought my luck had changed didn't actually start well. At the end of first break, Miss Bentley came up behind me, gripped me by the shoulders and pushed me towards the Tadpoles classroom. 'Don't be late, little one,' Miss Bentley said, in her I'm-speaking-to-the-babies voice.

At All Stars Primary School our classes are split up by the stages of a frog's life cycle. So Reception and Year 1 are Tadpoles, Years 2, 3 and 4 are Froglets and Years 5 and 6 are Frogs.

I am in Year 6. I am not a Tadpole, I am a Frog.

When I turned round, Miss Bentley's hand flew up to her mouth. 'Oh, I'm sorry, Pea— I mean, Anzo,' she said. Then she did one of those giggle-coughs that grown-ups do when they're not supposed to laugh but can't help it. 'I keep thinking you belong in Tadpoles, don't I?'

'Yes,' I told her.

Miss Bentley knelt down and fixed me with her big brown eyes. 'I am so, so, sorry,' she said.

'That's OK,' I said.

In case you're wondering, I was lying.

It wasn't just Miss Bentley pushing me towards the Reception class. It was that she'd been about to use the Nickname. She'd been about to call me 'Peanut'.

There are lots of names for short people, and I've been called them all – Smurf, Shrimp, Squirt, Shorty McShortShorts . . . but the one I hate most is 'Peanut'. When you're so short that people regularly think you're five years younger than you actually are, and when people can lose track of you when you're standing next to a traffic bollard, you don't want to be reminded of it every second of the day. And 'Peanut' is the kind of name that doesn't let you forget.

In the afternoon we had a school trip to Lyme Regis. We live in a small town near the south-west coast. Any time the teachers want to take us somewhere educational, they take us to the beach. (Everyone at our school is really, really good at rock-pooling.)

We all filed onto the coach and then Mr Dooley got on, walked to the middle and did his head count.

'Where's Anzo?' Mr Dooley called out.

Everyone on the coach started to laugh.

'What is it?' Mr Dooley snapped. 'Is Anzo off sick?'

'He's definitely sick of being small, sir,' Josh Gurney shouted out.

In case you haven't guessed it by now, Josh is not a friend of mine.

I got up from my seat and walked up to Mr Dooley. 'I'm right here, Mr Dooley,' I said.

Mr Dooley looked down. 'Where've you *been*, Anzo? You know we need to leave for the trip punctually if we're to get back in time for the end of school.'

The thing about grown-ups is that they aren't interested in explanations. Mr Dooley didn't even wait for my answer. He was already pushing me towards a seat. That's another thing about being short – people push you around all the time. They seem to think if you're small, your legs must need a helping shove.

'What you want,' Elise said as we walked down the beach, 'is a megaphone. You could use it whenever Mr Dooley is trying to find you.'

Elise and I have known each other since we were three. We couldn't stand each other then (she used to hit me over the head with her panda and I'd pelt her with my rhinoceros) but we've become friendly since we discovered that we both like comics. Also, Elise is quite small for her age.

'What I *want* is to be a foot taller,' I told her.

'You will be,' Elise told me. She said that every time I complained about my height. I didn't know how she could be so certain. In the last two years, my *nails* have grown more than my legs have.

Then on the beach, when we were supposed to be searching for signs of marine life (in other words, rock-pooling), Josh decided it was time for another 'joke'.

'Hey, Anzo, he'd make a good donkey ride for you.' He came up to us, pointing at a large dog in the distance, then ran off laughing before I could make some cutting comeback. Not that I'd thought of one.

'Ignore him,' Liam said. Liam is in our class and we're pretty friendly, though we don't properly hang out after school or anything.

But it's hard to ignore someone who doesn't want to be ignored. Josh was now making hee-haw noises up ahead.

To make me feel better, on the coach on the way back I got out my mini-notepad and did a drawing of Josh as a donkey with big, stupid, floppy ears. Revenge with a pen. Josh will never see it so maybe it wasn't actually much of a revenge, but it did make me feel better. Sort of.

The worst bit of the day was when we got back to school. Everyone raced over to the noticeboard. I remembered that the school-play details were being announced. I followed with Elise, but didn't bother trying to get close. When you only come up to most people's armpits, you know to stand back and wait.

'Hey, Peanut, congratulations,' Josh said. Then he cracked up laughing. Josh has a laugh that sounds like someone sucking up the end of a milkshake with a straw.

Elise and I looked at each other. 'Uh-oh,' Elise said quietly.

Uh-oh was right. It was never a good sign when Josh laughed. Josh's sense of humour is based completely on other people's misery. The more miserable someone is, the more hilarious he finds it.

Just to remind you, Josh is not a friend of mine.

We went up to the noticeboard. Miss Bentley is in charge of doing our school plays. After the first couple of years she stopped holding auditions. She said it was because she didn't want anyone feeling traumatised by the audition process. But everyone knows it's because she'd struggle to get anyone to audition because of what's happened before.

The sign took up almost the whole board.

Snow White and the Seven Dwarfs
Adapted and scripted by
Miss Amelia Bentley

Cast:
Snow White: Geeta Naskar
Sleepy, Grumpy, Dopey, Sneezy, Happy,
Bashful and Doc: Anzo Oliver

I didn't read past that bit. I'm not sure anyone else did either. It wasn't just Josh who was laughing now. Everyone in Frogs, everyone in Froglets and even some of the Tadpoles were laughing – and some of the Tadpoles can't even *read*.

'You're *all* the dwarfs!' someone shrieked before collapsing giggling on the floor.

'Hey, Dopey!' shouted someone else. 'No, I mean Sneezy – I mean Bashful! I mean, Sleepy!'

'No, he's definitely Grumpy!' Josh yelled, and then fell about.

I backed away – right into Miss Bentley.

'Oh, Anzo, you've seen the good news!' She

crouched down, flicking her long hair out of her face (Miss Bentley is a real hair-flicking type). 'I've written the most brilliant lines for you – and I've designed seven different hats for you to wear.' She tapped her lips with her fingers. 'I may have to teach you a few different accents too.' She beamed at me. 'This production is going to be a triumph, I just know it!'

Miss Bentley didn't seem to hear everyone laughing. She didn't seem to hear the last remnants of my dignity rolling across the playground and down the school drain. She didn't seem to see my look of complete and utter horror, or Elise's glare.

Miss Bentley is not a teacher who notices much.

I wanted to say no. I wanted to tell Miss Bentley that there was absolutely no way I was going to be *one* dwarf, let alone seven, but everyone was looking at me, laughing, apart from a few, like Elise and Liam, who were just looking sorry for me. My skin got hotter and hotter. I opened my mouth but couldn't speak. Elise pulled at my arm. 'Come on, let's go,' she said, as the bell rang.

Thank you for choosing a Piccadilly Press book.

If you would like to know more about our authors, our books or if you'd just like to know what we're up to, you can find us online.

www.piccadillypress.co.uk

You can also find us on:

We hope to see you soon!